Accreditation of prior learning for nurses and midwives

This book is dedicated to Professor Anne Hilton and the late Mike Taylor, with gratitude for their patience, kindness, friendship and amazing sense of humour during my early years in AP(E)L

Accreditation of prior learning for nurses and midwives

by

Wendy Nganasurian

Quay
Books

Mark Allen
Publishing Ltd

Quay Books Division, Mark Allen Publishing Limited, Jesses Farm, Snow Hill, Dinton, Nr Salisbury, Wiltshire, SP3 5HN

© Mark Allen Publishing Group 1999

A British Library Cataloguing-in-Publication Data
A catalogue record for this book is available from the British Library

ISBN 1 85642 129 5

Printed in the UK by The Cromwell Press, Trowbridge, Wiltshire

Contents

Acknowledgements		vii
Introduction		ix
Chapter 1	Nursing and midwifery education today	1
Chapter 2	An introduction to accreditation of prior and experiential learning (AP[E]L)	16
Chapter 3	A preliminary review of your AP(E)L potential	31
Chapter 4	Accreditation of prior certificated learning	42
Chapter 5	Making an experiential learning claim	52
Chapter 6	Examples of AP(E)L	70
References		91
Index		93

Acknowledgements

My thanks to all the students who worked with me as their AP(E)L adviser, particularly during the period 1993–1995. In the beginning we were all learning together and supporting one another. The majority have now attained good degrees.

Introduction

Despite the fact that accreditation of prior and experiential learning (AP(E)L) is growing in popularity, there appears to be very little literature targeted specifically at the student. One of the reasons may be that higher education institutions offering AP(E)L usually provide students with their own, institutionally individualised, handbook/ guidebook. While the principles of AP(E)L are the same, the way in which they are put into practice will vary between institutions, as will the precise use of terminology. Although this book will be of use to any health or social care practitioner who is considering putting forward an AP(E)L claim, it is intentionally focused upon the needs of nurses and midwives. There are a number of AP(E)L issues of particular relevance to this discipline and all examples have been taken from the claims of this group. It will also be helpful to nursing and midwifery educators who are asked to guide and support claimants during the process of presenting claims.

I believe it is important for employers/managers of nurses and midwives to appreciate fully not only the value of AP(E)L but the full extent of opportunities. Employers, in the form of trusts and consortia, purchase nursing and midwifery continuing education from higher education institutions (HEIs). There are opportunities to press HEIs to move beyond the current, more common usage of AP(E)L. For example, claimants are usually required to match each and every outcome of a specific module if they are to gain exemption with credit. This is not necessarily the most helpful approach for the profession (nor for the service provider/employer). In my own school, we created a partnership which enabled experienced nurses to register for a course, develop a portfolio evidencing those elements of a specific module which they already knew, and then drop-in-drop-out of a rolling programme of teaching which covered other elements of the module. This was particularly appropriate for, and attractive to, experienced nurses in critical and acute care settings who, for whatever reason, had never attained the relevant certificate. There are plenty of opportunities to recognise academic credit in respect of employer lead in-house training and, in my view, insufficient use of verbal evidence of attainment of relevant prior learning. An employer who is well-versed in the range of potential opportunities offered by AP(E)L can pressure educators to move beyond what is their current practice.

Nursing and midwifery — the pressure is on

My work as an AP(E)L co-ordinator and as co-author of an English National Board for Nursing, Midwifery and Health Visiting (ENB) commissioned project on assessment in AP(E)L (Skinner *et al*, 1997) convinced me of the need to demystify the subject for the student's benefit, and, in particular, to place it within the context of nursing and midwifery practice. Nurses and midwives are among the professional group making most use of the AP(E)L opportunity.

In August 1997, I retired as Dean of the School of Nursing, Midwifery and Professional Health Studies at Anglia Polytechnic University and this gave me the opportunity to write. I am a nurse (RMN, SRN) and I would like every nurse and midwife to have the chance to use AP(E)L because it is a wonderful opportunity both for individuals and the profession.

In 1996, there were 645,011 nursing and midwifery practitioners on the effective register (UKCC, 1996). 130,000 were over 50 years of age and a further 171,032 over 40 years. While there are many mature entrants to Project 2000 programmes, it is reasonable to assume that the greater proportion of those practitioners over 40 years commenced their education prior to joint accreditation, ie. a professional qualification (RN/RM) plus an academic award (diploma/degree). Therefore, AP(E)L is an ideal opportunity for this group. As I travelled around, talking to various groups about the related subjects of AP(E)L and professional portfolios, I became acutely aware of the pressures experienced by nurses and midwives in clinical practice today (Nganasurian, 1995, 1996).

Nursing and midwifery educators have survived change after change but our colleagues in practice have also been bombarded with role, organisational and service changes. Nurses/midwives frequently voiced their concerns to me about staffing levels, skill mix and the pace of work in their practice settings. Many were concerned about the issues of contracts and confidentiality. If higher education required them to think 'critically' about their practice, how might this be viewed by their employers? Some were confused, and sometimes irritated, by the way in which nursing and midwifery education has changed. There was a feeling of being devalued among those who completed their initial training course and some/all of their continuing professional development before it was associated with academic credit. For some, far from presenting new opportunities and facilitating their continuing education, the odds seem to be stacked against them. If they fought and won the battle for funding, and then gained a place on their chosen course, they had to contend with a mass of new terminology (eg. credit, dual accreditation, academic levels, modules, pathways, critical analysis) and acronyms (eg. APA, APEL, APL), a new style of learning which they were told was, apparently, the preferred style of adult learners, and unfamiliar assessment criteria. In addition, many felt under pressure to gain a diploma or degree because, although they had years of experience, they believed themselves to be at a disadvantage when it came to future career progression.

> Claimant A: A nurse with ten years experience in coronary care asked me who I would rather have care for me if, God forbid, I suffered a myocardial infarct. The choice she gave me was between a nurse with what she called 'a bit of paper' or herself. Skilled at opting out of such hypothetical questions, my answer was that my ideal would be to have one nurse with both the qualification and the experience. Theory and practice complement each other and are inextricably bound together if high quality is to be offered. With much encouragement from myself and a colleague, she finally signed on the dotted line and, through AP(E)L, was able to complete her degree in a far shorter time than someone 'starting from scratch'. She, and the university, were able to recognise the value of the experiential learning, to identify gaps in knowledge, to fill those gaps and to extend her boundaries of learning. When we met at her graduation (a professionally recognised award in coronary care was an integral part of her degree) she told me that she had gained a considerable amount from her course. She had met with colleagues from other hospitals and considered different practices. She had read more widely than she had done previously and started seriously to question more of her own assumptions, as well as those of the medical staff. She was convinced that her application of this knowledge to her practice did indeed enhance patient care. I told her that if I ever have that coronary I'd make a special request for her to care for me.

The National Board for Nursing, Midwifery and Health Visiting continue to accredit courses from a professional standpoint and, with the transfer of nursing and midwifery education to HEIs, have become involved in AP(E)L issues, eg. ENB Higher Award (1991) and 'Adding up the Past. APL/APEL: Guidelines for Good Practice' (1992). Not all HEIs were familiar with AP(E)L themselves when integration occurred and this left their new nursing and midwifery educator colleagues unprepared to face 'an army of nurses marching towards us, demanding academic recognition for all their previous work' (Skinner *et al*, 1997).

About this book

When writing, I am going to assume that while some readers already have a good grasp of higher education, others do not. Therefore, I will start from the basics and work upwards. In this way, you, the reader can skip or scan-read the parts you already know all about or just use them to reinforce what you know.

Each chapter follows the same format:

The chapter begins with a summary box, highlighting key points.

Throughout the chapter you will find that important words and phrases have been highlighted to emphasise their significance and for ease of reference.

You will find examples from practice including, with their permission, comments from ex-students and extracts from their work.

Most chapters conclude with a list of actions you may wish to take and/or questions to ask of your chosen higher education institution.

Terminology

Throughout the text, I am going to use the word **institution** when referring to any form of higher education institution (HEI), such as a university. I am going to talk about AP(E)L **claimants** when referring to those nurses, midwives and/or students who are considering or putting forward a claim and the word **course** when referring to a programme of study leading to a professional or academic award. The acronym APL refers to accreditation of certificated learning, APEL to experiential learning, and AP(E)L when referring to a combination of both. All other terminology will be explained within the text.

Coming to grips with AP(E)L

Put very simply, the principle of AP(E)L is: *just because something is a normal part of a course, you shouldn't have to study it if you already have the knowledge*. Therefore, AP(E)L can save you time, money and frustration, as well as valuing your past.

This breaks down into the following three main points:

1. Recognise that relevant learning may have taken place before a student embarks upon a new course.
2. Consider evidence of prior learning in the context of the new course.

3.   If assessment shows that the student has already covered some of the learning that will be offered within the new course then, in order to avoid repetition, academic credit can be assigned to his/her prior learning.

Most people have no difficulty with those three points, but it then becomes more complicated.

It is only when one comes to put the principles into practice that all the complexities become apparent. For example,

What is relevant?

What evidence is required to show that prior learning has taken place?

Does it matter how recent was the learning?

What proportion of an academic award can be attained through AP(E)L?

Once nursing and midwifery education became an integral part of higher education, still further complexities were introduced. This was mainly due to the nature of much of our prior learning. Simple principles, while laudable, were shown to be extremely difficult to operate, while the nature of work-based learning challenged academia in ways not previously foreseen. The nature of the relationship between HEIs and nursing and midwifery education is explored further in the ENB Project (Skinner *et al*, 1997).

There is no doubt in my mind that even though the principles are straightforward, and some complexity is inevitable, academics have got themselves so bound up with words, and the power of critique, that they cannot let any statement go by without dissecting it, complaining about the wording, and regurgitating it in some slightly different and more elegant form. There are few things more off-putting than being made, unintentionally or otherwise, to feel stupid and this has been a bone of contention in the eyes of some very experienced nurses and nurse managers.

A student came out of a lecture and, as she passed me, said 'he's brilliant isn't he [referring to the lecturer]. The problem is, I'm so stupid I couldn't understand a word he said'. This is a shame since the lecturer was meant to be teaching and that was, undoubtedly, what he thought he had been doing.

AP(E)L should become a transparent process, stripped of unnecessary jargon and complexity, if those entitled to credit are to come forward. Once we are familiar with something we wonder what all the fuss was about at the beginning.

AP(E)L — a special case

My AP(E)L mentors, Professor Anne Hilton and Mike Taylor, were very skilled and experienced, and both attempted to make higher education more user-friendly. Both retained the most incredible sensitivity towards the feelings of students. If students fail to pass an examination they are likely to feel regret, perhaps despondency, for a while. However, when claimants are involved in putting forward an AP(E)L claim for assessment (particularly one based on experiential learning), it seems to be so much more personal. Students are claiming knowledge and skills and someone is valuing it in academic terms.

> Claimant B: During the nail-biting wait for the results of an experiential learning claim this midwife said, 'If you claim you've got prior knowledge — well, if it gets rejected, it's as if you were lying'.

> Claimant C: A mature student who, no matter what reassurance was given and despite appeals to logic, still felt as if she was submitting *herself* for judgement. 'If they reject my APEL claim I'm going to feel far worse than I've ever felt when I haven't done well in a test. It's me that's being looked at — as if I'm having to prove I can do the job I've been doing all these years. And what if it's turned down? I have staff nurses working under me who have made successful claims — what will I feel like then?'

When I first became involved with AP(E)L, there was a fair amount of scepticism from some quarters and reference to 'letting people in (to higher education) by the back door'. AP(E)L is not a quick, easy option. Credit, as the saying goes, is only given where credit is due. An AP(E)L claim can be a lot of hard work and students need to realise this and be motivated to value their past through this means. Some maintain that it is a lot easier to take the module, despite it being a repetitious learning experience, rather than submit a claim based upon experiential learning.

> Claimant D: 'For the next ten weeks, my life was dominated by APEL... my sleep was interrupted frequently by spasmodic spells of inspiration. I was compelled to get up at odd hours to write.'

> Claimant E: 'APEL is not an easy option. It requires many hours of thought, work and organisational ability.'

However, it seems that, with support, it is worthwhile.

> Claimant F: 'Although it was hard to undertake such an extensive self-directed module [referring to the APEL module] I felt that I had achieved something positive at the end and that my experience had counted for something and was officially recognised.'

Claimant G: This is an extract from a note written by a student who was very near to the end of her professional career. 'The graduation ceremony was a proud moment... My thanks for giving me, in the autumn of my life, the opportunity of being awarded a degree.'

Claimant H: 'Just a short note to let you know of my progress. I completed my course of study and gained an upper second classification. I felt good.'

Sadly, Mike Taylor died in 1996, but his wife is happy for me to reproduce his poem 'Giving Credit'. It gives insight into his sensitivity for the feelings and situation of the claimant.

She sat in my room
And audited her life.
In the column 'wife',
Three husbands.
As mother,
Another and another and another.

Then a raft of low earning
Jobs to keep the family afloat
Evening classes to advance
Her learning.
Latterly the chance of a
Career. Caring.

Things were looking up
By degrees, as kids
Grew older, she'd
Re-claimed herself.
Writing in a folder.

So what was the tariff
For survival, solvency,
Kids that still knew love,
A job well done?
Twenty general credits
Level One.

(Mike Taylor, 1944–1966)

AP(E)L developments take place in institutions around the country and through consorita, eg. South East England Consortium for Credit Accumulation and Transfer (SEEC), and through funded projects. As nursing and midwifery educators become more confident in the use of AP(E)L and familiar with their HEI, there is a likelihood that, while academic standards will remain intact, the systems surrounding

AP(E)L will simplify. This will benefit claimants, the profession, employers and the institution itself.

Chapter 1
Nursing and midwifery education today

Summary box

1. Nursing and midwifery education is now an integral part of higher education within the United Kingdom. This has increased the range of educational opportunities available to nurses and midwives. In particular, there is now the opportunity to gain joint professional and academic recognition within some courses.

2. Many institutions operate a flexible credit accumulation and transfer scheme and are increasingly including part-time study, evening deliveries and open learning. This provides nurses and midwives with more opportunities to study while working full or part-time.

3. Most courses are divided into modules, each module being set at a particular academic level and carrying a number of credit points, depending upon how long it lasts.

4. When students have accumulated sufficient credits they are entitled to receive an academic award such as a certificate/diploma in higher education or a degree.

5. Prior learning can now be recognised for academic credit. This process, called AP(E)L, is made easier if the claimant has a sound understanding of the way in which courses are structured, their individual component parts, academic levels and regulations.

Good foundations are worth their weight in gold

No matter how tempted you are to get straight to the **accreditation of prior and experiential learning (AP(E)L)** parts of the book, I can promise you that they will be easier to follow if you have sufficient background knowledge about higher education. This book is written in a way that gradually builds up knowledge in a step-wise fashion. Ideas and issues raised in one chapter will appear again in subsequent chapters in order that these key issues may be reinforced and clarified. Repetition can be boring, but it certainly gets the point across although, as most parents with teenage children will confirm, it doesn't guarantee the desired response.

The building blocks of higher education

Nursing and midwifery education has changed in many ways over the last decade and, if it is new to you, the reader, I hope to be able to prepare you for what to expect. If you have recent experience of higher education you may want to skip this chapter or just to scan through it. Academia is complicated by the fact that higher education institutions do not operate in identical ways. This chapter will try to help you understand the principles and, thus, put you in a better position to go to the institution providing your chosen course and ask the right questions. It will also help you appreciate what they are asking of you and why.

Course structure

A minority of higher education institutions still offer relatively rigidly structured courses that have a continuous flow, with assessment at set progression points, eg. at the end of each year. Some do not take into consideration learning that has already been achieved. The majority, now operate a more flexible system called **Credit Accumulation and Transfer Scheme** (CATS). **Credit** is academic currency.

Number of academic credits

Institutions that operate CATS will normally offer small units of learning, usually called **modules**. Each module will carry a certain **number of academic credits** depending upon how long it lasts. Institutions do not all share the same view of how many hours make a module and how many hours of study result in one credit. One institution may offer its modules in 100 hour packages, each carrying 10 academic credits. In other words, if students study 10 hours they will have the equivalent of one credit out of the 10 available for that module. A module lasting 200 hours would give them 20 credits, assuming they pass the assessment, and so on. Another institution might work to a completely different **tariff**, eg. 75 hours:10 credits, and so you will need to check what system operates in your chosen institution. Of course, it is necessary to pass the assessment for any module before credit is awarded. It is not just a case of serving time.

While this might seem obvious to you, I have had one or two claimants tell me that they have completed a course worth 20 or 30 credits. What they have neglected to mention, through misunderstanding rather than intention to deceive, is that they, for various reasons, were not awarded those credits.

Levels of credit

In an institution that offers modularised courses within a CATS framework, students will find that some modules are more difficult than others. The level of difficulty (called the **academic level**) will normally be identified by the words 'level one, level two, level three, or level four'. Level one is less intellectually challenging than levels two, three or four. Level two is less challenging than levels three and four, and so on. Some institutions don't use all four levels, eg. they might combine levels two and three, and some call the levels by letters instead of numbers. Others refer to foundation, intermediate and advanced levels. Regardless of what they call it, the principle is the same. The assumption is that students don't study a level two module until they have gained a baseline of knowledge from a level one module in a related subject. Students would not normally complete a level three module in mathematics until they had completed a level one and a level two module in that subject, building up knowledge, ability to function independently, information retrieval skills, and improving their academic writing style. There will be more about this later when we talk about the effect of making an AP(E)L claim.

Learning outcomes

The title of any module should give students an indication of what it's about, but to get a better idea, students need to see the **objectives or learning outcomes** for that module. At the end of a level one module they may be asked, for example, to 'describe a nursing model', whereas if it was a level three module they might be asked to 'critically analyse the contribution to patient care made by nursing models and cite examples from your own experience'. When writing learning outcomes, different verbs are often used to reflect different academic levels. For example, at level one, students would be expected to be able to retain given information and present it in a modified form. This might mean reading something and **drawing conclusions** from it. It might mean showing that they have understood something by explaining it in a different way or applying it to a particular situation. Generally, what is required is somewhat **imitative** and **descriptive** in nature. While much of the information needed for the student to 'describe a nursing model' is available in textbooks, it is obviously more challenging to 'critically analyse', requiring students to:

- probe the subject
- debate the comparative values of different models
- consider use of a model against no model at all
- give examples based on experience
- argue the case convincingly.

This higher academic level requires the student to show a greater ability to **analyse, evaluate, demonstrate advanced reasoning and logical thought processes, draw new insights, recognise underlying assumptions and then consider their validity or lack of it**. For students to attempt this, it will require wider reading and more thought.

Academic writing skills

There are a number of textbooks available on this subject and your chosen institution may even offer a special short course or module dedicated to helping those new to, or returning to, higher education. Academic writing is different from report writing. Those assessing students work will be looking at the way they express themselves in writing, how clear the meaning is, how fluent the style, how well they have grasped important points and how effectively they have argued their case. In addition, spelling, sentence construction, punctuation, and general presentation will be considered. You may, for example, be told to refer to yourself as 'the author' whereas you may be more used to writing the word 'I'. Some students complain that the content is less important than the written style but, although it may seem this way, there are complex issues surrounding academic standards across the higher education sector.

Accumulating credit

It is still possible to study any of the many ENB professionally recognised awards, sometimes referred to as the 'numbered awards', eg. ENB 997/8 (Teaching and Assessing in Clinical Practice). These constitute valid, professionally relevant, learning but they normally carry between 20 level two academic credits — 90 level three academic credits, depending upon the award. On their own, while they are very worthwhile **professional awards**, they carry an insufficient number of credits to merit an **academic award**. The reasons for this will become clear as you read on.

Students can accumulate academic currency (**credit**) by studying those small units of learning (**modules**), just as they can accumulate another type of currency, ie. money, by working and saving. When they have accumulated enough academic credits they can exchange them for an academic award.

This is rather like working a number of weeks in order to accumulate money in the piggy-bank until there is enough to exchange for a holiday. One might, for example, save vouchers/stamps in a book until one has enough to exchange for a gift.

Academic awards are called **certificates, diplomas, degrees**. Students studying for any one of these three awards would be called **undergraduates** because their particular combination of modules, sometimes called a **pathway**, is below the level of, or building up to, a degree. They will, at some point, probably **graduate** with a **first degree**. The award will be conferred at a graduation ceremony and hence they are undergraduates until then.

When a university operates CATS, students will find that they gain an **academic award**, eg. BSc or BA, according to how many credits they have accumulated. Once again, the precise detail may vary between institutions but the majority operate along the following lines.

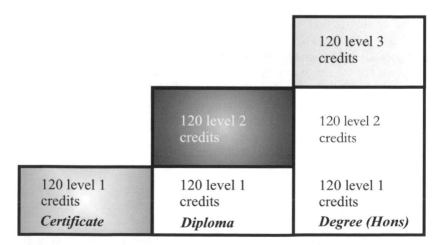

Figure 1.1: Accumulating credit for an academic award

Although some courses still have a very tightly constrained structure and content, sometimes because of professional body regulations, there are an increasing number of opportunities for students to tailor all, or at least some, elements of their course to their unique requirements. Courses are often shown as having both **compulsory** and **optional or elective elements**. In some institutions, individualised academic awards are designed, in their entirety, by individual students according to individual needs. In other words, all elements are optional/elective.

Postgraduate studies at level four lead to either a postgraduate certificate, postgraduate diploma, or **higher degree** (usually called a **Masters**), depending upon the number of credits accumulated at this level.

The title of the academic award will, just like a module title, tell students what is in it and who is likely to study for it, eg. BSc (Hons) Engineering or BSc (Hons) Health Studies.

Dual accreditation is possible, eg. a student registers/indexes for both the academic award (from a higher education institution) and the higher award/specialist practitioner (from the ENB). Sometimes triple accreditation is possible, eg. a national vocational qualification (NVQ) has been incorporated into a professional/academic award.

Classification

The percentages that students achieve in their assessments will have an effect upon whether they are awarded a first, second or third class honours degree. There are even different grades within these categories, eg. upper second, meaning the average mark was at the upper end of the range in which a second class honours is awarded. It is normally only the assessments associated with a proportion of the coursework that contribute towards the actual classification of a degree, eg. the best 180 credits at level two and three. Once again, different institutions use different methods of classifying their students awards. In *chapter 2*, I will explain how AP(E)L can influence the outcome of classification.

Transferring credit

The advantage of CATS is that, in the same way that people can change their minds over a holiday destination, students can change their minds over the final award they want to achieve or even the institution in which they want to study. However, the transfer value of academic credits (just like money) will vary, depending upon the course or institution to which the student transfers. Changing one's mind is not something that should be considered lightly but sometimes changes in one's career or family circumstances force a change. There may be particular problems if one is fairly near the end of a course because, even where the opportunity exists for a fully **negotiated academic award**, it is likely that one will come up against various regulations concerning how much credit can be 'imported' to an alternative course. If, for example, a student was only 20 credits away from completing his/her degree at his/her original institution, (institution A) it is unlikely upon transfer to another institution (institution B) that s/he would be permitted to gain a degree by just studying for the remaining 20 credits. After all, the degree will have institution B's name on it but nearly all the learning took place in institution A. How few or how many credits the student has to take to achieve the degree will be determined by institution B.

What to expect if you are new to higher education

Venue

Although some nursing and midwifery education is still delivered on hospital sites, perhaps in one of the classrooms that constituted the old 'school of nursing', it is increasingly likely that students will need to travel some distance to study. Traditional higher education students, ie. 18 year olds on a three year full-time course supported, in part, by state funds, tend to live on or near to the institution's campus. However, there are an increasing number, particularly the growing number of mature, self-funding, part-time students, who travel daily from their homes and family commitments. In fact, over recent years, more 18 year old school leavers have chosen to live at home rather than go away to university because it is cheaper.

This commuting creates parking difficulties and I received more complaints about this than anything to do with course content or teaching. Just as David Nobbs character called Reginald Perrin always blamed the trains for being late, students tend to blame car parking for their late arrival at classes. Unsympathetic teachers, like me, simply say, 'Well, get here earlier to get a space'. Students who study in institutions located in town or city centres may find the only parking is in public car parks. They may find that it costs up to £10, or even more, to park for a day. Some institutions recognise this problem and lay on special transport on certain routes. In addition, the buildings that make up the institution may be spread across a town, or even wider, and necessitate the use of public transport or 'shanks's pony'. Once a student has found a parking space s/he is very unwise to move his/her car just to travel to the next lesson. Generally speaking, gone are the days of nipping easily across from the ward to the classroom and back again. In the institution where I worked, there were times when students had to travel up to 90 miles to take part in a specific module.

Flexible Learning

Greater flexibility in higher education has resulted in more learning opportunities being made available at weekends, evenings, through distance learning and the internet. Although many courses still start in September (the traditional start of the academic year), there are an increasing number that are offered with alternative start dates. This enables more nurses and midwives to take courses since their employers cannot release them all on one date.

For instance, in the institution in which I used to work (Anglia Polytechnic University) we offered nursing and midwifery students the opportunity to register for an academic award that gave them the opportunity to study at their own pace, in their own homes, using materials that could be relatively cheaply purchased from high street shops or the institution, and with the added bonus of being able to pay as they learned rather than at the start of the course. In addition, the individual student was able to negotiate the submission date for any piece of work s/he intended to submit for assessment purposes. The course proved particularly attractive to those who needed to attain a certain level of credit before they could enter a top-up degree. Many nurses and midwives cannot get sponsorship in the form of either time or money from their employers and this kind of flexibility offers them the opportunity to meet their continuing education needs.

Interdisciplinarity

Most of the 'old' schools of nursing are now departments or faculties within a higher education institution and the nurse tutors are called lecturers. Nurses and midwives are, however, increasingly likely to be taught by non-nurses/midwives. They are more likely to share classes with other students studying anything from engineering to social work if and when the topic is relevant to more than one discipline. Communication studies could, for example, be seen as equally relevant to nurses/midwives, doctors, engineers, lawyers and social workers. There could be considerable benefit to be gained from sharing different experiences, while applying the knowledge to one's own field. Sometimes classes are so large that rooms are linked by monitors, the lecturer being in another room.

Once students get used to this style they frequently find it's more enjoyable than taking a very rigidly time-tabled course with the same nursing/midwifery colleagues, taught by the same small group of nursing/midwifery teachers, and in the same room each week. It is important to find out where and when teaching takes place and to consider travel, which can take up quite a large part of the day.

A new style of learning

Some students find that the amount of time they are expected to study on their own is far greater than they are used to. Students might have only one or two sessions lead by a lecturer and a greater number when they are asked to work with peers, study alone or prepare for a tutorial or assessment. This level of '**self-management**' and independence can be daunting if students are used to a more directed approach and some people experience a sense of isolation and a feeling of 'not being cared for'. You will find terms like 'student centred learning', 'adult learning' and 'discovery learning' being used to describe this independence. Such terms usually imply that while you will be provided with the means to learn, nobody will spoon-feed you. Once students have made the transition from more directed learning to self-managed learning they are generally far more satisfied.

> Claimant A: This student had qualified as a nurse 15 years ago. He had progressed in his career and was the charge-nurse of a busy medical ward. He had joined a course in September but by January he was complaining bitterly that it was 'useless'. He told me he wanted his fees refunded because he had 'expected to be taught and not to have to do-it-myself'. When he elaborated, it was clear that he meant he expected a teacher to stand in front of him telling him, in effect, what he could have read in a book. He maintained that he wasn't learning anything using this method and that the staff were more interested in 'getting information out of their students' than in teaching. Clearly his expectations had not been met and he felt frustrated and let-down.

Generally speaking, the greater the depth of knowledge the more independent students are expected to be. Therefore, whereas students on a traditional three year degree might have fairly frequent contact with lecturers in their first year, this would become progressively less as the end of the course approaches in year three. Students would, by that time, have learned how to use the library and information technology efficiently, have developed the self-discipline to pace themselves, be able to exploit the system of peer and tutorial support and have finely tuned their intellectual skills of analysis and reasoning.

Once you have adjusted to this self-managed style, you will find it frustrating if a lecturer is more directive. I recently attended a study day on legal issues. Being a good student, I read the materials sent out before the day, undertook the suggested supplementary reading, and prepared my list of what I wanted to know. I felt, for once, nicely prepared for the event. However, the lecturer simply went through, word-for-word a lot of the time, exactly what was in the pre-course materials which she had forwarded to all students. One or two fellow students actually wrote it all down (again). The lecturer then gave us a handout with the information in it (again). My questions were answered with comments like, 'It would be better to ask your legal adviser about that'. As you can imagine, my evaluation form took quite a long time to complete. That mismatch between my expectations and learning style and that of the lecturer delivering the study day resulted in what I saw as a lost opportunity, but one or two participants seemed quite pleased with the day. On the point of note-taking, it surprises me how many mature learners still take notes by writing down as much of what the lecturer says as is humanly possible. There are books on the subject of effective note-taking (often combined with study skills) and they are well worth reading. A few hours spent with this type of book can save a lot of time and effort later.

Assessment

Students receive, probably in written form, information about academic writing, including the type of **referencing system** the institution requires, eg. Harvard, and the meaning of the academic crime of **plagiarism**. It is quite easy to fall foul of the 'law' simply by having an ill-disciplined note-taking technique. For example, a student may be reading a book and jotting down important sections, sentences, etc. At a later date, when taking part in a written assessment, that student may incorporate those notes in his/her essay. However, if, at the time of first jotting them down, s/he didn't make a note of the source of this information, ie. the author, date of publication, where it can be found, it becomes incorporated into his/her work as if it were his/her own thoughts or words.

Institutions will require a certain **standard of written English** (as already explained) and may insist upon assignments/projects being word-processed. It may all seem, at first, to be somewhat petty. Despite what you might read in the press, it isn't true that 'anyone can get a degree nowadays'. In my view, it is more accurate to say that good preparation can prepare most people in such a way that, with the right support and motivation, they can gain an academic award. That is different.

Students will probably be allowed two chances at an assessment. This is less likely to be an invigilated examination nowadays and more likely to take the form of a lecturer-marked assignment which students have a number of weeks to prepare. Use is increasingly made of student presentations to, and judged by, their peer group or some form of self-assessment. If students do feel unfairly treated then they can make an informal complaint or a formal appeal against the way their teaching and assessment was carried out. However, it is important to acquaint oneself with the official means of complaining and the timescales that influence it.

One improvement in education today is that, increasingly, the **criteria for marking** are made clear to the candidate before s/he submits work for assessment. In the past, there seemed to be considerable room for individual marker preferences. Nowadays, most lecturers are asked to mark against specific criteria which are made known to the candidate and which the candidate can use when preparing work for submission. This takes some of the uncertainty out of assessments.

One further point on assessments. If you know that you suffer from some learning difficulty, such as dyslexia, you should make this known to your course leader as soon as possible. Ideally, you should disclose this at the point of course selection. This will not exclude you from studying but it will mean that resources can be brought in to help you deal with the potential difficulties. If you have a major problem that negatively influences your performance in a particular assessment, you should make this known immediately (don't wait to know whether you did well or not) because it may be possible to give you a further opportunity to take the assessment when your circumstances are not adversely affected. All these issues are likely to be covered, in detail, in course and institution documents/leaflets that you will be given. It is very important that you find the time to read them even though you are longing to concentrate on the real subject matter of your course. As a nursing student, I never read these kind of things. However, I would definitely read even the small print nowadays.

Payment

The arrangements regarding payment of tuition fees and living allowances for full-time higher education students are still under review. While most pre-qualifying nursing and midwifery students have, like other full-time students, applied through a central clearing system, their fees and allowances are slightly different. If you are one of those readers who intend to give up their post, if they have one, and take up full-time, self-funded, education, my suggestion is that you consult the University Central Admissions Service (UCAS)* or one of the institution's advisers who can guide you through the application process and financial situation. In this way you will get the kind of advice a school careers guidance officer would provide to the traditional candidate, ie. the A level student.

By far the greatest number of nursing and midwifery students are undertaking studies directly related to the discipline and will be self-funding or sponsored by their employers. You may wish to find out from your manager how to go about getting a sponsored place (NHS trusts, via education consortia, have contracts with certain institutions to provide a specific number of places each year on particular courses).

Obviously, a manager will look more favourably upon applications from staff who appear to be knowledgeable about their chosen course and how they will manage the learning within it. If they have previously shown themselves to have good attendance, and not only have a pass record on previous courses but have been seen to apply the knowledge and skills to their current practice, then managers will see money can be well spent on that employee's education. However, if a manager has no funding left, or a student particularly wants to undertake a course at an institution with which his/her employer has no contract, then the employer may agree to give that employee the time off if s/he pays his/her own fees. Students may have to pay fees all in one go but it may be possible to pay by stages, sometimes called 'pay-as-you-learn'.

Whichever way fees are going to be paid, students will need to recognise that, although there will be a library, they may need to buy books and will probably need access to a word processor. In addition, there is the cost in terms of time. If a course says it lasts for 30 hours this doesn't mean that is the time students will spend studying it. Particularly when students are new, or just returning, to higher education, there is a tendency seriously to underestimate the amount of time they will spend on self-managed course-work, including assessments.

Not starting with a blank sheet

When students commence their studies at any point other than with zero credits, they are either admitted with what is called '**advanced** standing' or, if the institution operates CATS, they are '**admitted with credit**'. Those students will not be given any form of special dispensation or help to enable them to meet the necessary standard to gain a pass grade in later assessments. Therefore, it is up to those students to ensure that they have sufficient background knowledge and academic skills. They might, for example, talk to other students who have done, or are currently on, the course, always remembering that everyone is different. They may benefit from gaining or refining their skills in word-processing before embarking on the course. They may undertake a specially designed 'return to study' programme or attend sessions aimed at helping people new to an academic style of writing. In many institutions, one can register for a single module so that one can see if one will enjoy being a student again, before signing up to a greater commitment.

There are degrees that are advertised as '**top-up' degrees** and these are specially designed to meet particular needs. For example, an institution may have recognised the need for qualified nurses/ midwives who hold a diploma in higher education (Dip HE) in a nursing subject to 'top-up' to degree level and so they will offer a specially tailored course. These claimants are presenting their prior learning, ie. Dip HE, for accreditation in the context of the 'top-up' degree. Others who do not hold the Dip HE may be able to undertake the same 'top-up' degree by using other kinds of prior learning as their entry point. AP(E)L is a means to obtaining 'admission with credit' since claimants are asking for their prior learning to be considered against their chosen course. More of this in *chapter 2*.

It is most important for students, to be successful, to plan ahead and organise not just their holidays around course dates but also when and how often they will study each week. Preparing a study setting, getting all the materials needed and agreeing with family and friends 'seclusion' times are all useful ways of gearing up to return to study. Failure to plan ahead is an all too common reason for dropping out of a course.

Once students are on a course they will probably have a personal tutor allocated to link with them on non-subject specific matters. This academic may remain constant throughout their course whereas other teachers come and go, depending upon which module the student is studying. There will be a Student Union for advice and social activities, a chaplaincy and a counselling service: all of them are there to help students benefit from their higher education experience.

Higher education is great fun and quite addictive if one selects the right course, prepares oneself for it and determines to get the very best out of time, tutors and peers.

> Claimant B: Gemma had it all sorted. She had obtained a funded place through her employer and had presented her AP(E)L claim with due regard for when her course would start. She had read many of the set books for the first few modules well before the course had even started. She had gone to evening classes to learn word-processing and her in-laws had purchased a computer for her as a birthday present. Gemma had organised her duty-rota well ahead and was taking annual leave to coincide with the institution's Christmas and Easter breaks. Two months into the course she announced that 'the hand of fate has struck' and she was pregnant. Throughout the summer period she sat in swelteringly hot classrooms, having brought in her own electric fan. She was never late submitting assignments. She continued to study even when she was no longer able to work in the care of the elderly setting. Her partner brought in her final assessment, stating that she had been breast feeding while giving him instructions as to who he should hand her work to and he was not to come away without a signed receipt for it. Gemma was motivated and, in her words, 'Come hell or high water, I'm getting this'.

Questions and actions

1. Does the institution operate CATS and, if not, how are their courses structured?
2. If the institution operates CATS, what is their tariff (how many hours per credit)?
3. Are you eligible for the course you have selected and are all the component parts compulsory or can you choose which modules you take?
4. When does the course start and finish and what is the maximum length of time you can take to complete it?
5. Is there a particular sequence in which modules must be taken?
6. What academic level is your course set at?
7. Check that the content of the course is right for your needs.
8. Does the award carry dual accreditation?

9. Find out:
   i) where modules will be delivered
   ii) if there is a particular day of the week on which teaching takes place
   iii) what time do sessions normally start and end
   iv) if the institution makes any special transport arrangements or allocates parking spaces?
10. Can you have your prior learning accredited in the context of the course you want to study?

*UCAS handbook and application form, with a range of information booklets, can be obtained from UCAS, PO Box 28, Cheltenham, Gloucestershire GL50 3SA.

Chapter 2

An introduction to accreditation of prior and experiential learning (AP[E]L)

Summary box

1. Both prior certificated (APL) and uncertificated/ experiential learning (APEL) can be reconsidered/assessed in the context of their relevance to the particular course a claimant wishes to embark upon.

2. The academic credits that are awarded for prior learning can help claimants enter a course for which they are otherwise ineligible and/or, if the prior learning is relevant to the new course, they can be used as an integral part of that award or to substitute for learning within it.

3. Neither claimants nor academic staff can tell if there is a valid AP(E)L claim to be made unless the claimant has:

3.1. Self-knowledge
A clear idea of the knowledge and skills s/he has achieved through either certificated or experiential learning.

3.2. Course knowledge
A decision has been made regarding which course s/he intends to study. (Information on the range of courses offered by an institution can be found in their prospectus. However, if an applicant is unsure about which course is most appropriate it is usually possible to get advice over the telephone or through an appointment with a member of academic staff.)

3.3 Compared 3.1 with 3.2 above
Undertake a preliminary mapping of the learning already achieved (3.1) against that normally achieved through the course chosen (3.2). This will provide a starting point for making either a certificated learning claim (APL) or an experiential learning claim (APEL).

---

4.   When claimants make a prior learning claim they will be required to present evidence of the learning in order that an assessor (someone familiar with both the area of their prior learning and the new course) can consider the relationship between that which already exists and the new. A claimant will receive help in the form of either written guidelines on how to make a claim or through telephone/face-to-face contact with a member of academic staff, usually called an AP(E)L adviser.

5.   Claimants will normally be charged for the support and assessment but a successful AP(E)L claim can reduce the amount of time, and hence money, needed to complete a new course.

6.   It is, generally, easier to make a claim based upon prior certificated learning than on experiential learning. However, it is in the field of experiential learning that many nurses/midwives have gained a wealth of knowledge to underpin their skills or to update prior certificated learning. Therefore, nurses/midwives are potentially higher users of APEL.

What is AP(E)L?

Higher education institutions acknowledge that learning takes place in situations other than just in their own classrooms and that some students have already covered material that is within that institution's courses. Careful consideration of such prior learning enables the academic achievement to be teased out.

Learning may take place in different situations, ie:

- in a classroom
- in the workplace
- through life experience.

Academic credits attained through accreditation of prior and experiential learning (AP[E]L) can be used for different purposes. These include:

1. As **an alternative entry gate** to higher education (instead of the traditional A levels). Although AP(E)L may be used to enable students to commence a course for which they would otherwise be ineligible, it is rarely used in this way by qualified nurses and midwives, unless they are changing career track.

2.   As an **integral part of an academic award.** Academics spend a long time debating the issue of **general v specific credit.** Each institution obviously believes that the way in which it uses these terms is the correct way. Fortunately, claimants don't have to understand fully the nature of this argument nor to agree with the way in which the terms are used. However, I will provide a very simplistic outline of the issues.

In nursing and midwifery education, credit from prior learning may be used to recognise the **relevance/significance of learning** already achieved and to make this an integral part of an award, eg. prior learning may enable nurses/midwives to embark upon 'top-up' academic awards or to take their careers in a more 'specialist' direction. For example, the institution may accept prior learning that is related to the themes within an award, rather than requiring prior learning to match identically with elements of the course. Themes within an award might be, for example, communication skills, interpersonal relationships, clinical nursing practice, or teamwork. Some institutions permit students to use credits from prior learning as an alternative to the optional/elective elements of the course.

Using prior learning credits in this way is sometimes referred to as **general credit** but, in some institutions, it would be called **specific credit.** These latter institutions might argue that it is possible to recognise a general credit value for every piece of learning that has ever occurred in an individual's life. However, since only a proportion of that general credit is relevant/significant in the context of the course chosen by the claimant, the term specific credit is more appropriate for all types of **admission with credit.** Fortunately, claimants are more interested in whether they are awarded credit than what it is called.

3.   To **substitute for specific learning** that students would normally get by attendance in the classroom or practice setting once enrolled on specific modules.

Prior learning may have to be very tightly matched to the outcomes of very specific modules normally taken by students studying for the particular award. Under these circumstances students must have learning that closely matches that shown in the module outcomes. This would, for example, be necessary if the outcomes were closely related to patient safety in a particular context and where professional recognition was associated with the award. This type of credit is usually called **specific credit.**

Through AP(E)L, more people are able to access the benefits of higher education and avoid boredom and time wasting. Thus they may achieve their chosen qualification in a shorter time. This can reduce the cost to themselves and/or their employer.

Different types of AP(E)L

Two types of learning can be presented for accreditation purposes. They are:

1. Prior learning that has already undergone rigorous assessment and has resulted in a certificate from an academically reputable organisation, eg. the ENB. This is normally referred to as **accreditation of prior learning (APL)**.

2. Prior learning that has not previously been assessed for academic purposes. This includes all learning that does not fit into category one, such as learning from experience and through short courses, study days and in-service training.This is normally referred to as **accreditation (or assessment) of prior experiential learning (APEL)**.

When referring to both or either type of learning, a commonly used term is accreditation of prior and experiential learning (AP(E)L). As you might expect, not all institutions use the same acronyms when referring to these two types of learning. Sometimes accreditation of prior achievement (APA) is used; sometimes APL refers to both certificated and experiential learning; sometimes APEL refers to accreditation of professionally evidenced learning. Throughout this book APL refers to certificated learning, APEL to uncertificated/ experiential learning and AP(E)L to a combination of both. If you decide to make a claim it is important to check with your chosen institution the meaning of acronyms used but not explained.

Getting the credit

APL

To achieve academic credit, students must be **assessed**, regardless of whether they sat in a classroom or claimed they already had that knowledge. If students have already been assessed as part of a course leading to a certificate, then the content of that course and the evidence of achievement, ie. the certificate, will need to be considered in the context of the new course.The most usual way of presenting evidence of **prior certificated learning** is to present the certificate and the course related information. This will be covered in more depth in *chapter 4.*

> Claimant A: Jenny had worked in various in-patient settings for six years and wished to work in the community. She used her RMN, RGN, ENB 998 and A30, plus three modules on research to attain the 240

credits she needed to begin the BSc (Hons) Community Specialist Practitioner award.

APEL

Because this type of learning has not previously undergone a recognised form of assessment, this must be done before academic credit can be given. The assessment is as rigorous as the more traditional assessment methods chosen by an institution. As with any type of academic assessment, claimants may be given a time scale for submission and may be permitted only two attempts at making a successful claim. Alternatively, the institution may take the view that claimants should pace themselves and can keep submitting until they have sufficient evidence to convince their assessors that they have the knowledge.

There are different ways of presenting **evidence of prior experiential learning** for assessment.

One option, if you believe that you have already gained the knowledge a specific module expects to teach, is to complete the assessment that normally accompanies that module. Sometimes claimants say that this is easier and quicker than trying to find evidence for certain, less tangible, knowledge and skills, eg. communication. This option may be referred to as the '**challenge method**'.

A more common method of submitting evidence of prior learning is to submit a **portfolio**. There are different types of portfolio and a **professional portfolio** is different from a portfolio submitted specifically for AP(E)L purposes. The latter is, more importantly, specifically designed to show prior learning **in the context of the course upon which the student wishes to embark**. It may contain many types of evidence of learning such as certificates, testimonials, care plans, articles, teaching materials and projects, along with an explanation of the meaning of these artefacts, both in the context of the knowledge claimed and of the new course. This will be described in far greater detail in *chapter 5*.

Rules and regulations

AP(E)L is true recognition of prior learning but in the context of a particular academic award and within the regulations of a particular higher education institution. These regulations may, for example, prohibit the inclusion of AP(E)L credits over-and-above a certain number, eg. 50% of the total for the award. This figure will vary from institution to institution. There may be a regulation about claiming for learning that has already resulted in an academic award of the same level as the award that the student intends to study, eg. a claimant already has a degree in nursing but wants to use some of the credits to achieve a degree in health studies. This is sometimes called '**double-counting**'.

Claimants will probably find that there are time limits on the 'shelf-life' of certificated learning, although they may be able to show that their work experience and reading has kept the learning alive and up-to-date. Since no two institutions are identical, claimants are well advised to ask these questions about regulations as early as possible and, thus, avoid frustration and disappointment.

The process of assessment/accreditation

Prior learning, whether certificated or uncertificated/experiential, is not as easy to accredit in the context of a particular academic award as some people might think. The whole process can be completed in a matter of days (usually when the certificated learning is clearly identical to elements of the new course), but it may take weeks or even months for an experiential learning claim to pass from start to finish.

A more detailed account of presenting a claim in respect of certificated learning can be found in *chapter 4* and in respect of experiential learning in *chapter 5*. However, the following provides an introduction to the different roles of the participants in AP(E)L.

The claimant's role

Know yourself

It is essential that a claimant has an appreciation of his/her own knowledge and skills and how they have been developed through courses or experience. It is surprising that so many nurses and midwives have little or no appreciation of the wealth of their own expertise. Very experienced nurses/midwives can be very poor at what we might call 'celebrating their own knowledge'. *Chapter 3* will explore the whole area of identifying learning.

Know the course that you intend to study

While potential claimants can seek advice from their managers, other nurses/midwives, and from nursing and midwifery educators, it is ultimately their own responsibility to ensure that the courses they choose are the right ones. Claimants cannot tell whether they have valid AP(E)L claims until they have decided which course they intend to study because their prior learning must be judged **in the context of a**

particular module/academic award. Most institutions now offer a wide range of courses leading to an equally wide, and often confusing, range of academic awards. In *chapter 3*, I will explain how to decide which course is the most appropriate.

Identify relevant prior learning

Having considered both prior learning and the learning normally attained through study of the new course, the claimant needs to identify where the two map onto each other. For example, a claimant may have, through various short courses and clinical experience, gained knowledge of leg ulcer management equivalent to that covered by a module within the course s/he intends to study. This would constitute a valid APEL claim.

> Claimant B: This student telephoned me and began to reel off a long list of qualifications. Since she seemed to do this without the need to draw breath, I couldn't stop her. At the end she took a deep breath and added quickly 'I want to know what it's worth?' It was impossible for me to tell her because the first step had been missed, ie. what course does she wish to have her prior learning considered against? Nobody can map prior learning against thin air; there must be something to map it onto. 'No', she said, 'I don't want to do a course — I just want to know what it's all worth?' This is a total misunderstanding of the purpose of AP(E)L, unless she had a particular reason for wanting a general credit rating. I explained that many of the certificates she had referred to would, if taken today, carry considerable academic credit but, since she had completed all of them in other institutions, and some of them a very long time ago, each one would need to be scrutinised closely. She said she could send me all the certificates but hadn't retained any course materials such as the syllabus, assessments, etc. If it had been possible, and appropriate, for me to undertake a general credit rating, it would have taken hours, days or longer. The next question would be who would pay and was it worth this effort and expense? In the end I sent her a prospectus, highlighting those courses I felt might be suitable. Three months later she returned, having chosen a course and then we were able to consider her prior learning. However, it is the student who has to undertake initial mapping and present this as a claim. While I would provide the necessary information it is for the student to do the work and put forward a convincing case for credit.

Collate and present evidence

It is part of the claimant's role, as applicant, to put forward a claim, not that of a member of university staff. It requires time and effort on the applicant's part, collating evidence and putting forward a case for why the learning is relevant and how it articulates with the particular academic award. While claimants will be given help and advice, it is in their own interest to provide **relevant materials** in a sufficiently logical, succinct manner to enable someone who doesn't know them, and probably will never meet them, to place their learning **in the context of their chosen award and to determine its academic credit value.**

Claimants learn many things during the process of AP(E)L, including self-awareness, eg. their ability to tolerate uncertainty in novel situations. When they reflect upon their AP(E)L experience they frequently say how, although it may have been a difficult transitional period, it prepared them for future studies. In fact, many students do extremely well in their later studies and exit with very good degrees. Further evidence of this will be provided in later chapters.

AP(E)L adviser's role

The university will have identified someone who can offer claimants advice and guidance in submitting an AP(E)L claim. This person is usually called an **AP(E)L adviser**. Claimants may need a single, initial meeting or a number of meetings, particularly if they are presenting experiential learning. If they are making a claim for prior certificated learning alone they may simply be given written information on how to present their claim. If they are making a substantial experiential learning claim, they may be offered the opportunity to join a group of claimants engaged in the same activity. Sometimes this group support takes the form of a credit-rated module, from which the credits can be used towards their award, in addition to those from their prior learning. A good adviser can help a claimant develop analytical skills by asking challenging questions. S/he can advise on academic writing skills and point the claimant in the right direction to get any help that is needed.

AP(E)L assessor's role

An **AP(E)L assessor** is usually a member of academic staff who has experience in assessing claims of this type. S/he, in the case of nursing and midwifery education, is likely to be a specialist or subject expert in the area of the claim s/he is asked to assess. In addition, s/he will normally have experience in teaching and assessing students studying on the course to which the AP(E)L claimant is seeking entry. In this way s/he can judge both the strength of prior learning and its relevance in the context of a new course. The assessor is able to compare a claim of prior knowledge and skills with the knowledge and skills s/he would expect to see in students who study the new course/module.

The process may also require that the claims and the recommendations of the AP(E)L assessor are considered by a number of committees before a final decision can be given. This can take many weeks and so it is important that claimants present their claim well ahead of the date that they wish to start their course. It is possible to make an AP(E)L claim once a student has commenced a course, but it is more usual to make it before the start.

Claimants support network

Claimants who have previously made successful AP(E)L claims can be invaluable to new claimants. I used to hold a list of ex-claimants names and contact numbers which, with their permission, could be given to new claimants. If such a list is not available in your institution, ask around your colleagues and try to find someone in this position. They will probably enjoy talking about their AP(E)L experience but, remember, everyone is different.

The price of AP(E)L

From what is written above, you can see that it is rarely, if ever, just a question of a quick telephone call, even in the case of APL. The charges to claimants vary between institutions. Most charge less for APL than APEL, while others charge a flat rate. Some charge 'by the credit': in other words, the more credits claimants gain through AP(E)L, the more they pay. Some charge the same for AP(E)L as for the module, had a claimant attended in the traditional way. Some charge one price for APL but another if it is not straightforward and has to be supported by evidence as to how the learning has been kept up-to-date. Sometimes charges for AP(E)L are included in the sponsorship money from employers but this is not always the case.

Whether you get value-for-money is not just dependent upon the adviser. You need to analyse your own learning needs and match these against what you are getting. If they do not match then address the issue, if necessary, by talking to the adviser and seeing if there is any way that more help could be given or different support techniques used.

AP(E)L issues

Context relevant credit

Generally speaking, nurses and midwives are reasonable people, but there are always one or two who do not hear what is being said. I have encountered angry people who resent the amount of credit they have been awarded, seeing it as a personal slur, because they have not fully understood that AP(E)L has to relate to learning **relevant to the academic award**. They would not expect an engineer to get 240 credits for his/her prior learning in automotive engineering when s/he decides to take a health studies degree. AP(E)L must never be seen as a convenient way of gaining one piece of paper after another and is definitely not 'a quick fix'.

> Claimant C: Cilla, a very experienced theatre and orthopaedic nurse, decided to change track and become a district nurse. Although the title of the academic award she intended to gain was BSc (Hons) Community Specialist Practice, she couldn't, at first, understand why she was not accredited with the full volume of general credit associated with her theatre and orthopaedic training. Obviously, much of the learning within these courses was also relevant to community practice, eg. interpersonal skills, infection control, and post-operative care, but other elements were less relevant. Academic staff have to consider the overall balance of learning within an academic award and ensure that the title is a true reflection of the learning, however the credit was attained.

Experience *v* experiential learning

Life-long-learning is something of a catch-phrase at the moment. There are, of course, individuals who go through an experience and do not learn from it. I am sure we all know people who have attended a lecture and mentally drifted off for most of it, resulting in little learning taking place. Undoubtedly, we can also recall someone who underwent an experience but who appeared to miss the whole point of what was going on and simply repeated their mistakes the next time around. Perhaps you know someone who has worked in a job for 20 years but seems only to have attained the learning that another individual has gained in three years in that same job. This is why 'time served' in any potential learning situation cannot be used without evidence of the quality of learning achieved.

Claimant D: A very irate charge-nurse told me he resented having to present evidence of his years of service. In his own words, 'Why should I have to prove anything'. While I didn't doubt that he had worked for those years, I couldn't assume that he had expanded his knowledge and skills year-on-year, nor could I assume the areas in which his knowledge and skills would equate to particular levels of academic credit. Part of this charge-nurse's anger was as a result of misunderstanding of the purpose of AP(E)L but it was partly due to his feeling that he was being left behind in the dash, as he saw it, to get a degree. When he calmed down, it was possible to tease out a wealth of learning that had taken place over the years, including some very valuable project work initiated and completed by him.

Lack of confidence

Throughout my time as AP(E)L co-ordinator, and during the project work for the ENB, I continually encountered nurses and midwives who lacked confidence in putting forward their own knowledge and skills. The expression 'I don't suppose it's worth much' regularly preceded an elaboration upon extensive knowledge in a particular field. The application of theory to practice and the generation of theory from practice was evident, despite the fact that the nurse or midwife was putting him/herself down with expressions such as 'but all my colleagues can do that'.

Claimant E: One of the best APEL claims I have ever seen came from a nurse who had never undertaken a formal management course but who had read widely and applied what she had learned to a particular reorganisation project. She was very sceptical about her chances of making a successful claim because it involved 'management' and in her own words, she was 'only an F grade'.

Consider the consequences of an AP(E)L claim

One word of warning: nobody *has* to make an AP(E)L claim, and there may be times when it may not be in someone's best interests to do so. Consider, for yourself, what effect the claim will have, over-and-above all the benefits already described. Is there any chance that it puts you, the claimant, at a disadvantage to other students in subsequent modules?

If, for example, a claimant knows, in all honesty, that s/he is a little rusty in an area which is assumed to exist, then this can cause problems. For example, a registered nurse/midwife qualification is frequently recognised for 120 level one credits (the equivalent to the first year of study in a new course) and so the first module on research methodology is pitched at level two. However, while others in the class may have had the benefit of an introduction to basic research in year one, the AP(E)L claimant would be disadvantaged if s/he found that the terminology was confusing and felt s/he was getting left behind. That claimant could remedy this situation by being very open with the AP(E)L adviser about these concerns. The adviser will let him/her see a level one research module in order that s/he can make a realistic appraisal of his/her level of prior learning. The adviser might suggest supplementing prior learning with some additional reading or the student might do better to seek 110 level one credits, and take a 10 credit, level one research module as part of his/her new programme of learning.

Nobody *has* to make an AP(E)L claim against a module that looks really interesting even though they could match its outcomes through prior learning. What claimants cannot do is attain prior learning credits as a result of matching that module and then study the module as part of their course. This is another form of '**double-counting**'. Hopefully, a claimant would not decide to study a module s/he could have matched through a prior learning claim just because s/he will probably find such a module easy and get a good grade as a result (thus improving upon the final degree classification). A more valid reason would be because studying with a different peer group, plus new experiences, will consolidate prior learning and add a new dimension to it.

Claimants are wise to consider what impact shortening their period of study will have on course funding. It is possible that, if they are going to be a full-time student on a grant, they could jeopardise their income if they claim sufficient credit through AP(E)L to reduce their course hours of study below the level considered to be full-time.

Even when no grant is involved, students need to consider the impact of AP(E)L. Student F provides a good illustration of this point.

Claimant F: One very misinformed midwife thought that her employer would still permit her to take the days as 'study days' when she had AP(E)Lled out of a number of modules! It was not that she intended to spend these 'free' days in some wonderful leisure pursuit. She had planned to use them for reading and preparing her assignments for the modules she was studying and thought, quite rightly, that this would benefit the results she gained in those modules. Her employer quickly disillusioned her. She could, of course, have checked whether it was possible to substitute modules, thus avoiding the choice between AP(E)L or having to sit through modules she could have matched (repetitive learning). Unless all modules were compulsory within her chosen award she might have been able to substitute modules whose content would be equally relevant to the award, but new to her.

The wheelbarrow full of evidence

Some claimants think that they are more likely to be awarded a high number of credits if they submit, as evidence, everything that they can lay their hands on. The ability to **select out relevant learning**, supported by **relevant evidence of its achievement**, is another sign of academic ability. I have been handed cardboard boxes full of papers by smiling nurses and midwives who have taken a great deal of time and trouble putting everything together. However, I didn't have the time to sit with them and go through each item asking 'Why have you included this? What does it say about your knowledge? Where does it map onto your new course?' Far better that I receive a much smaller and more **manageable portfolio of well thought out evidence, with a written commentary that gives me information on why items of evidence were chosen, what they show and what they map onto.**

Many times, I have received a **professional portfolio** through the post (very expensive) with a letter that basically says, 'Here is my career. I have spent weeks compiling this file — have a wander through it and see how much you can give me for it'. Heed my warning and save yourself, and others, a lot of effort and disappointment. A professional portfolio is a statutory requirement for nurses and midwives but it is only the starting point for an AP(E)L claim. Because AP(E)L must be relevant to an award one can only use a professional portfolio as the basis upon which an AP(E)L claim can be designed. By looking through a professional portfolio areas of excellence and expertise can be seen. These may give an insight into the areas around which an AP(E)L claim may be made and then this can be compared with the course selected. The professional portfolio can then become a valuable source of individual items of evidence, eg. certificates, letters, other documents (see *chapter 3*).

Giving up

Claimants give up making an AP(E)L claim for various reasons but, in my experience, the commonest are listed below.

1. The claimant makes a claim for legitimate learning but for which there is little hard-and-fast evidence. This is particularly true when the claim is for experiential learning. When this is the case the student might wish, as an alternative to the portfolio method, to consider completing the standard form of assessment that is normally submitted by students studying the module, assuming that the institution permits this.

2. The claimant has too many things going on at once and fails to allow sufficient time to make a successful claim. This is often based upon the assumption that, because the claim is about what the claimant already knows, it will be easy to make a claim. Good advice at the beginning of the APEL process should forewarn the student. Unless the student is AP(E)Lling in order to enter a course at a particular point it may be that the credits sought through AP(E)L can be claimed later in the course, thus providing the student with an extended deadline. However, it should be noted that other assessments from other modules will still be due and, unless the student develops a highly disciplined study schedule, it is likely that work will continue to pile up.

3. The claimant lacks familiarity with academic writing and has difficulty adjusting to this style. The claimant might make a very successful APEL claim a little later in his/her course, once s/he has developed this technique through studying other modules. Alternatively, undertaking an academic writing skills module, if available, would help.

4. When an AP(E)L claim (in particular an APEL claim) is rejected when first presented, some claimants become extremely despondent, taking the whole thing personally. I used to have a notice in my office which read:

    'If you have made mistakes... there is always another chance for you... you may have a fresh start any moment you choose, for this thing we call "failure" is not the falling down, but the staying down.'

    (Mary Pickford, 1893–1979)

AP(E)L is one of the best opportunities around for nurses/midwives and available evidence suggests that we are, rightly, utilising it more than any other professional group because of the way nursing and midwifery education has been structured in the past. Experiential learning, in particular, gives the lie to some people's simplistic views of the complexity of our roles.

Questions and actions

1. Does your chosen institution permit AP(E)L in the context of your chosen course/award?

2. Which acronyms are used to describe certificated and uncertificated/experiential learning?

3. What is the maximum credit that may be attained through AP(E)L in the context of your chosen course/award?
4. How much will it cost you to make an APL claim and an APEL claim?
5. What help can you expect when making an AP(E)L claim?
6. Ask your employer, assuming you are being sponsored for your course/award, whether the cost of AP(E)L is included or whether you will have to pay for this yourself? A good bargaining point is that if you gain accreditation of your prior learning, you will complete the course in a shorter time and reduce the amount of replacement cost to your employer.

Chapter 3
A preliminary review of your AP(E)L potential

Summary box

1. By now you should have a grasp of the following from reading *chapter 1*:

    i)   the principles of credit accumulation and transfer schemes (CATS)

    ii)   how the number of academic credits is arrived at

    iii)   how academic credits can be accumulated to result in an academic award such as a certificate, diploma and degree

    iv)   the different levels of academic credit

    v)   how level one is different from level three

    vi)   the meaning of the term ' learning outcome' and how an outcome relates to an academic level.

2. You should have grasped the following from reading *chapter 2*:

    i)   the meaning, as used throughout this book, of the acronyms AP(E)L, APL and APEL

    ii)   the difference between AP(E)L for entry purposes and AP(E)L as an integral part of an award

    iii)   the reason why it is important to consider which course you want to take before submitting an AP(E)L claim

    iv)   the difference between a) undergoing an experience for a number of years and b) experiential learning

    v)   the process of making an AP(E)L claim

    vi)   the difference between a professional portfolio and one for AP(E)L purposes

3. In this chapter we will consider five interrelated areas when making a preliminary assessment of whether you have a legitimate AP(E)L claim. These five activities are:

Activity 1. Identifying prior learning

Activity 2. Making decisions about future career developments

Activity 3. Analysing strengths and weaknesses in respect of current role and future career

Activity 4. Choosing a course

Activity 5. Comparing the prior learning to that offered on the course.

The activities are normally undertaken in the sequence shown above. However, on occasions the sequence runs 2, 3, 4, 1, and 5. Sometimes an employer sponsors an employee for a particular course and there is no other course available to that employee. Under these circumstances, time and effort can be saved by only seeking out and identifying prior learning that is directly relevant to the course which will be taken (activities 4 and 5). The claimant considers the award title, module titles and their learning outcomes first and then seeks to equate these to what s/he already knows or is able to do. To go through a full and lengthy professional review would, under these circumstances, be an added bonus but not essential if time is at a premium. The sequence below assumes that there is a range of courses open to the student and s/he is responsible for determining which is the most appropriate to his/her needs.

Activity 1: Identifying prior learning

If someone was to ask you, 'What have you learned since you qualified as a nurse/midwife?' the answer would probably be, 'Em...'. It is extremely difficult to identify the learning that has taken place because there has, generally speaking, been so much of it. If the question was, 'What do you know now that you didn't know before you qualified?' it may be slightly easier to respond but the problem is still one of volume of learning. For this reason, it is helpful to begin a personal and professional review of learning by breaking it down into the three steps shown below.

Of course, the process of professional review will be familiar to nurses and midwives because we are obliged, under Post Registration Education and Practice (PREP) requirements, to maintain a professional profile. Practitioners are, through their profile documents, required to satisfy the United Kingdom Central Council (UKCC) that they are appropriately qualified, safe and up-to-date. Some nurses and midwives have taken this a stage further and chosen to develop a more extensive and in-depth review within a professional portfolio, rather than a profile. People in this latter group may find that they can simply look back at their professional portfolio for the information needed for steps 1 and 2, and possibly 3 of this activity. A professional portfolio is a very useful document at this stage of AP(E)L because, although it is very different from an AP(E)L portfolio, it provides the necessary initial review of existing knowledge and skills. Whether a professional portfolio exists or not, the following steps need to be taken in order to identify prior learning.

Step 1: A description of experience in the form of roles and dates

This is no more than creating a list of **jobs/roles** and the relevant dates. It looks a little like the beginnings of a curriculum vitae. In the examples below I have made certain changes in order to protect the claimant's identity and that of places in which she has worked.

Claimant A: Charlotte

'I qualified in 1980 as a Registered Mental Nurse. I trained in a fairly big hospital in the south-west. From 1980 to 1982 I worked as a staff nurse in an elderly care setting in the same hospital where I trained. In 1982 I started my general nurse training and qualified 18 months later as a Registered General Nurse. In 1984 I married and, because my husband got a job in the north of England, I took a post as staff nurse on an acute admission ward in a very large traditional psychiatric hospital. In 1987 we moved back to the south, and I got a job in another hospital. I was staff nurse in an acute admission unit. I had my first child in 1988 and went back as a part-time staff nurse, working in a variety of settings, until the birth of my second child in 1989. My husband got a job in Newcastle and I gave up work until 1994 when we divorced and I moved back to the south-east. In 1994 I became staff nurse in an admission unit and took on special responsibility for patients admitted following self-harm. I was promoted to F grade sister in 1996. In 1997 I was promoted to G grade sister still with special responsibility for self-harm clients.'

Step 2: Adding further details

These include, responsibilities, characteristics of client groups, special opportunities and experiences that presented themselves. **Elaborate on this list of roles** by describing the client group in more detail and any special opportunities (including courses), responsibilities or experiences. This is still descriptive. Two examples are shown below relating to two episodes in Charlotte's professional career.

Example 1: 'In 1984 I married and, because my husband got a job in the north of England, I took a post as staff nurse on an acute admission ward in a very large traditional psychiatric hospital.

* patients with varied mental health problems
* patients in acute psychotic states
* specialising in drug and alcohol problems
* various study days on substance misuse
* read a lot about substance misuse
* went to xxx hospital to visit detox. unit
* postnatal disorders
* care of mothers and babies
* two suicides on ward
* liaison with other disciplines and relatives
* detoxification programmes
* AA group established
* behavioural contracts
* group and individual psychotherapy
* individual and family counselling
* social skills training
* went on a two day SST course
* managed ward for shifts
* went on ENB 998 in early 1987.'

Example 2: 'In 1994 I became staff nurse in an admission unit and took on special responsibility for patients admitted following self-harm. I was promoted to F grade sister in 1996.

* patients with varied mental health problems
* patients from ethnic minorities
* patients who had overdosed
* varied age groups
* work with relatives
* self-mutilation
* risk assessment
* close and special observation
* Mental Health Act
* individual counselling
* went on a three day cognitive therapy course

* six week (one day/week) counselling course
* groupwork
* drama therapy
* art therapy
* social skills training/assertiveness training
* went on a six week AT course
* teaching
* teaching up-date course
* team leadership
* in-service training on ward management
* visits to other mental health units with specialist self-harm settings
* time in A & E looking at self-harm issues
* completed ENB A30 1996.'

By this point, Charlotte was beginning to get a clearer picture, in her own mind, **of those parts of her experience that had resulted in the greatest learning**. Some of the experiences had been repeated again and again and, therefore, the opportunity had existed to learn more. For example, Charlotte had the opportunity to develop skills in social skills training (SST) and assertiveness training (AT) during 1984–1987 and to build upon these from 1994 onwards. She recognised that she had taught a number of other staff in this area through their co-leadership role in the SST groups she facilitated. Other experiences had not been repeated in this way but the experience had been intense and the learning curve had been steep. On the other hand, Charlotte recognised that, although she had the opportunity to engage in art therapy under the guidance of a qualified therapist, she had limited knowledge in this aspect of therapy. While she would feel confident to participate in both art and drama therapy, she would certainly not feel confident to take on a lead role or to teach others. However, she would feel confident in respect of SST/AT.

Step 3: Identifying the learning that was gained

Having completed step 2, it is necessary to be more explicit about the **learning** in respect of those areas in which an AP(E)L claim may exist. This is becoming more analytical. I have used one example from Charlotte's account. This example relates to the area of SST and AT. Writing learning outcomes isn't easy and even the academics find themselves criticised when colleagues scrutinise their work in this area. Therefore, it is not surprising that claimants need help to get started and, at this point, I wasn't too concerned about Charlotte's wording. In *chapter 5* we will explore, in more detail, the importance of wording.

Areas of knowledge and skill = social skills training/assertiveness training

I know:

* what social skills are and how to recognise assertive behaviour
* what the result of different patterns of behaviour is likely to be
* how to help others see their own behaviour and its consequences
* how to set up and run a group for clients
* more about myself and the effect my behaviour has on others
* how to carry out an individual assessment of skills and plan an individualised programme
* how to cope with various situations in a SST group including clients becoming very emotionally distressed, guilt feelings, hostility towards other members
* how to stop individual members taking over or dominating the group and how to encourage others who are quieter
* how to direct role plays
* when a group is going well or not
* how to analyse why things aren't going well
* the place of fun and laughter within these groups but recognise when this is not helpful
* how to rechannel negative feelings and how to help clients motivate themselves to keep trying
* how to work with a co-therapist and the importance of working well together
* the importance of planning before any session and of debriefing afterwards
* how to start and end groups
* the importance of following up clients who have completed a course
* why people stop coming.

Clearly, Charlotte felt quite confident in running such groups and knew that her knowledge of the subject and experience in it gave her the ability to train other professionals. An important question for Charlotte was, '**Do you still know or did you once know**?' In other words, is this knowledge still alive and well and as relevant today as it was when you attained it? While a professional portfolio is able to reflect knowledge that is no longer 'alive' (or in need of advanced life support), an AP(E)L claim can only be made in respect of current knowledge. In respect of nursing and midwifery education, the word '**current**' also means up-to-date since the knowledge base of our profession changes quite rapidly and what was considered fact in 1960 may have been shown to be false in 1998. Consider, for a moment, how the following four care issues have changed in the light of new knowledge:

i) pressure area care

ii) nursing care of patients following myocardial infarct

iii) salt in the bath

iv) length of stay in surgical settings.

The ways in which these are dealt with now is very different from 1980.

Activity 2: Decision making about future career developments

Some people drift in various directions without appearing to have any control over where their career is going. While this passivity may suit some, it is likely that many nurses and midwives have an idea of whether they wish to remain in clinical nursing, specialise in a particular area, move into education, or focus on management. This self-knowledge helps to direct one to courses that can help further these plans. It is a good idea to talk to people who already hold a post/s that one might be interested in: ask them questions about the good and the bad parts of the job; the kind of knowledge and skills they need to fulfil that role.

In Charlotte's case, she knew that she wanted to remain clinically focused. She was very confident in this area. However, because clinical grading was linked, rightly or wrongly, with status and financial reward, she recognised that she had to maintain the management role which she didn't particularly like. Ideally, she would have liked to move into the field of clinical research but recognised that jobs were difficult to come by.

Activity 3: Analysing strengths and weaknesses in respect of current role and future career

As a result of the professional review carried out in Activity 1, claimants become aware not only of **those aspects of their job which they do well but of those areas in which their knowledge or skills are less well developed**. By looking, honestly, at both our strengths and weaknesses we can determine what we need in order to perform our current role more effectively and to increase our chances of moving our career in the desired direction. This helps to determine the most appropriate course and, where there is room to choose, to select personally relevant modules.

Charlotte lacked confidence in areas such as budget management and thought she could do better in respect of motivating colleagues. She had discovered a love of research but had very limited knowledge in this area. She also felt that the service offered to her clients could be improved but was unsure of how to go about planning, organising, managing and evaluating a project of this type. Therefore, her ideal course is one in which she can gain credits for her prior learning but include, as new learning, the psychology of motivation, research methodology and project management.

Activity 4: Choosing a course

It can be extremely confusing when one looks at the range of courses/awards/titles that are on offer from one or more institutions. Therefore, deciding which to take can seem like a game of chance, the hope being that one hits upon a course that meets one's needs and expectations. While choice will be influenced by career intentions and analysis of strengths and weaknesses, there are other determinants. Choices may be limited by financial considerations or by something as simple as the site on which a course is taught, the day of the week or the time. It may be that one's line manager or employer will only give time off if the course pursued is deemed by him/her to be relevant as determined by performance review.

I usually advise potential students to start by ruling out those courses for which they are not eligible. This information is usually found within a prospectus and may include qualifications required before entering the course, number of years experience or access to clinical learning opportunities during the course.

I advise potential students to make a list of any particular issues in respect of their choice of course. These should be categorised according to whether they are essential, highly desirable, preferred or they don't really matter too much. If, for example, a student is only able to undertake a course that is going to be funded by his/her employer then this comes under the category of essential. A student might prefer to take a course which is taught within a ten mile radius of his/her home but wouldn't rule out a course if s/he had to travel further, particularly if it meant having the opportunity to study a particular module that the student classed as highly desirable. A student may place in the highly desirable category a course which enables him/her to pick and mix modules rather than follow a standard prescribed pathway.

I also advise students to make an honest decision about what they can cope with. In *chapter 2*, I talked about AP(E)L issues and how making an AP(E)L claim can affect studies. For example, if a student chooses a course with a lot genetics, physics and chemistry in it then it is likely that s/he will need a certain level of mathematical ability.

By doing some careful thinking at the 'front end' of a programme of studies, the student is more likely to end up on a course that suits. This is very important because s/he is going to make a huge investment in both time and possibly money. Everyone knows how difficult it is to stay motivated if a course falls short of expectations or proves too difficult. Claimants are usually advised to make an appointment to talk to their line manager or employer about education plans. Sometimes this opportunity arises at annual appraisal or performance review. They are far less likely to get a well considered response if they corner their manager at a chance meeting or in the car park at 10 pm. Many institutions offer an advice service. Alternatively, it may be possible to contact a member of academic staff by telephone in order to find out more about the courses. I used to get a number of calls from nurses and midwives who simply put the ball in my court and asked what course I thought they should take. Without knowing what they had already done, what they wanted to do, or what they could afford, it was impossible to do this over the phone. If an interview was needed, this could take up to an hour and, eventually, I had to charge for such meetings.

Activity 5: Comparing the prior learning to that offered on the course

As previously explained, whether a claimant can put forward an AP(E)L claim depends not only upon whether s/he has **relevant knowledge and skills** but also whether the education institution offers the opportunity to use that prior learning. In *chapter 2* we looked at issues such as double-counting and how there may be a ceiling of credit that can be attained through prior learning. In both *chapters 1 and 2* we saw how course design impacts upon AP(E)L potential. Some courses leave little room for choice (eg. optional/elective elements), while others enable students to choose all the modules and to negotiate the final award title. It may, as already mentioned, be possible to submit a claim which results in **general credit** because it is relevant to the title of the academic award and is accepted in place of optional elements of the course. Other learning may need to match very **specific modules** within the course before it can be accepted.

By looking at the award title, the module titles and the module learning outcomes it will become clearer whether a claimant has relevant prior learning. This activity is called **mapping**.

To illustrate mapping, I will use an imaginary award entitled 'Certificate in craftwork'. This imaginary course consists of five modules, each carrying 20 credits. Their titles are:

Module 1: Teaching crafts to adults
Module 2: Flower arranging
Module 3: Embroidery
Module 4: Calligraphy
Module 5: Optional module (student to choose one of the following: pottery, pen and ink drawing, stencilling or basket work).

Claimant A holds a City and Guilds teaching certificate and has taught calligraphy to children at summer camps and adults in evening classes for three years. She might choose to register for our course because she wishes to study flower arranging, embroidery and pottery (taken as her optional module) but she would be very bored if she was required to attend all the sessions in modules 1 and 4 because of her prior learning. However, she will need to present evidence that her learning is equivalent to that which students who study teaching crafts to adults and calligraphy will attain upon completion of those modules. In doing so, she will be required to show that her knowledge and skills are of an equivalent standard/level and are up-to-date.

Claimant B seeks exemption from embroidery on the grounds that he has been doing cross-stitch, a type of embroidery, for many years. However, the module outcomes require students to be able to do several different types of embroidery as well as patchwork, quilting and tapestry and to be conversant with both the history of embroidery and technical matters such as the qualities of different threads. Therefore, by looking at the course outcomes and contents claimant B can see that it would be better to seek permission not to attend the individual sessions on practical cross-stitch rather than try to gain exemption from the whole module. If, on the grounds of prior knowledge, he submits a claim for exemption from the entire module it is going to be rejected on the grounds of insufficient evidence.

Because all institutions, and even different courses within the same institution, have different requirements, it is essential for potential claimants to seek out the answers to the questions at the end of *chapters 1 and 2* before going beyond the stage of an initial feasibility review if they wish to avoid wasting time.

Questions and actions

1. Consider your own prior learning (both certificated and uncertificated/experiential) through the three steps described above under activity one.

2. Consider your own career intentions and what knowledge and skills you already have that increase your chances of achieving your goal (activity two).

3. Consider your weaknesses, gaps in knowledge and what type of modules might address these (activity three).

4. Obtain a prospectus and choose courses that could suit your needs (activity four).

5. Compare your prior learning to the knowledge/skills offered within the chosen course/s. Is there a match? Do you have an AP(E)L claim (activity 5)?

6. Make an appointment to discuss your future education needs with your manager.

Chapter 4

Accreditation of prior certificated learning

Summary box

1. Certificated learning refers to learning evidenced by possession of some form of **testament,** such as a certificate or diploma.

2. Accrediting prior certificated learning is often referred to using the acronym *APL* (accreditation of prior learning), although different institutions may have different acronyms for this activity.

3. Responsibility for both evidencing **achievement** of prior certificated learning and showing its **relevance** in the **context** of any intended course of study lies with the student.

4. For APL purposes, academic credits can only be awarded if a student was **assessed** to see whether s/he had achieved the course aims and objectives **before being issued with the certificate**.

5. Learning from **courses with no assessment** *is frequently classed as uncertificated learning and is covered under experiential learning claims (APEL) because it is* **difficult to prove learning took place**. Some institutions will permit the claimant to write an essay similar to that presented by students on a present-day course leading to that certificate. In this way, the claimant can evidence **achievement of learning.**

6. A claimant needs to present the person with responsibility for APL with the **original certificate** (or a replacement if this has been mislaid). Photocopies are normally acceptable in the first instance, particularly if the general postal service is used.

---

7.   To help match prior learning with an intended course and, therefore, determine appropriate credit in recognition of past achievements, a claimant should decide for him/herself and then provide the institution with any/all of the following **relevant documents**:
    i)   certificate
    ii)   copy of the syllabus/curriculum (if not available send a written summary of content)
    iii)   statement pertaining to mode of attendance, eg. part-time
    iv)   timetable, showing duration of course, frequency of study days/blocks, and private study (if not available send a written account)
    v)   information concerning the nature of assessment, eg. a claimant may have been required to present four assignments and sit one unseen examination
    vi)   examples of assessed work, together with marks and comments, where available.

8.   Where a certificate has been held for more than five years it will normally be necessary to provide additional materials showing how a claimant has kept his/her knowledge/skills updated, eg. through work and subsequent education.

When is a certificate not a certificate?

The *Collins English Dictionary* (1991 edition) defines a certificate as 'an official document attesting the truth of the facts stated ... **completion** of an academic course'. A diploma is defined as 'a document conferring a qualification, recording **success** in examinations or **successful completion** of a course of study'. What, you might ask, is the difference between a certificate and a diploma. The main difference implied above is that you have to complete your course successfully in order to gain a diploma whereas you just complete the course for a certificate.

Add to this the fact that, as you have read in *chapter 1*, in academic terms, the words certificate and diploma have very clear and different meanings relating to a progression/completion point, ie. 120 and 240 credits respectively, and you can see why there is confusion over the term '**certificated learning**'. This confusion is worsened by the fact that some short courses issue a letter confirming attendance, whereas other organisations issue rather grandly titled certificates and diplomas after exactly the same type of course.

I have heard it said that, within higher education, frequently, there seems to be an overemphasis on the precise use of words for no apparent reason other than pedantry and 'one-upmanship'. This isn't the case in APL because it is essential that everyone shares a common understanding of the two words — **certificated learning**.

What is certificated learning?

In APL terms, this is learning that is demonstrated through possession of a document which testifies to both the **quality of the course and the claimant's achievement of its aims, objectives or outcomes**. The prior learning, evidenced by this document, can then be considered in the context of other learning, ie. the course the claimant wishes to embark upon. Therefore, there are four important points:

1. Standards
2. Evidence of achievement of outcomes
3. Date of completion
4. Context in which the claim is made

1. The course must be recognised as of an acceptable standard

When one studies on a course, there are various factors which govern learning. These include:

  i)   the syllabus needs to be appropriate
  ii) the teaching needs to be of a high standard
  iii) reading materials and other resources need to facilitate progress.

In other words, the quality of the course needs to be high.

The **quality of the course** may be testified by the fact that it was **approved** (sometimes called **accredited**) by a nationally recognised body (called the **awarding body**), eg. a professional body or a UK higher education institution (HEI) such as a university. A course seeking approval from an awarding body will go through various stages before permission is granted to offer that course. Details of the curriculum, duration of course, resources, teachers, teacher to student ratio, and so on will be considered before granting approval and, even after this, there will be regular monitoring to ensure standards have not slipped.

This is not to devalue a certificate issued by a less well known organisation or one with a less established reputation for high standards. However, more information may be needed to verify the credentials of that organisation and those who teach on its behalf. Claimants will be asked to provide as much course material as possible so that whoever has responsibility for APL can consider the way the course was structured, sequenced and its content in both breadth and depth. However, it is the claimant him/herself who must make that initial appraisal of the match between his/her prior learning and the intended course of study. Sometimes claimants try to unload everything they have retained from a course onto the desk of the person with responsibility for APL. The assumption is that s/he will wade through it all trying to find a match and identify relevance. This would be very costly to the institution when you consider that hundreds of claimants might be doing the same thing. It shows no analytical skills on the claimant's part and these are important in higher education.

2. Evidence of achievement of outcomes

Some form of assessment must have taken place in order to testify that the claimant achieved the aims and objectives of that course. Even if a course is of high quality and one was required to attend every day, if one is not motivated to learn, or the information and its manner of presentation is beyond one's grasp, it is unlikely that all the course aims, objectives or outcomes will be achieved. Therefore, merely having attended a high quality course does not mean that learning has taken place.

Planned learning experiences vary in length from a couple of days to three or four years. Normally, when one is only required to attend for one day this is called a **study day** rather than a **course**. Do two days constitute a course? Whatever your view, it is more than likely that no formal assessment takes place in courses of such short duration, eg. under two weeks. Therefore, the testimony issued at the end of such a course is, in reality, a **statement of attendance** since there is no proof that those who attended did, in fact, learn.

In the past some short professional courses, eg. ENB 997/8, did not require the student to be assessed. The certificate itself read 'statement of attendance'. This implied that, while the quality of the course could be assured (the ENB being a nationally recognised professional organisation), so long as the participant had been present in the room/ practice setting, taken part in the various learning activities and made satisfactory progress, then s/he would be issued with the certificate. In reality, most teachers delivering these short courses carried out rigorous assessment to reassure themselves that learning had taken place. Only then did they put forward participants' individual names to the ENB in order for the 'statement of attendance' to be issued. Some claimants have been enthusiastic squirrels and have retained samples of assessed work which is useful in these circumstances.

If assessment did take place, but a claimant has no proof, some institutions will permit him/her to sign a statement relating to the manner in which s/he was assessed, or obtain some form of confirmation from the establishment at which s/he studied that assessment did, in fact, take place despite the wording on the certificate. Institutions may offer the opportunity for a claimant, who cannot satisfy them regarding assessment, to write an essay similar to that for assessment written by students on a present-day course leading to that (or a similar) certificate. Some will insist that an experiential learning claim be made since the course was, strictly speaking, uncertificated learning.

3. Date of completion

We are all capable of forgetting and the less frequently we need to remember information, or use a skill, then the more likely we are to forget it. In addition, what is taught on a course will change over time in the light of new information and altered practices. It is for this reason that whoever is responsible for APL will be concerned if the date on the certificate suggests that the content is out-of-date or possibly forgotten. A course completed within the preceding five years will normally be considered as alive and well.

Some claimants have found that it is difficult to convince others that certificates issued more than five years ago are still worthy of APL, particularly in the light of rapid and continuous change in the knowledge base of nursing and midwifery and its subsequent impact upon practices. A claimant who has attended a course more than five years ago may have subsequently maintained the **currency of learning** through study days, reading and experience. In these circumstances, it is as if the original course in question provided a foundation of knowledge and the claimant has built upon that since then. In the the period since gaining the qualification, s/he has kept his/her memory refreshed and kept abreast of changes that would be covered in the present-day version of the same course.

Imagine that it is 1898 and Ethel is studying a course called 'Laundry'. If we were to ask her, assuming that she was still alive, how a present-day version of the 'Laundry' course differs from the one that she completed, she would probably say it has more technology, biochemistry etc in it. However, if Ethel had been working for the past hundred years as a laundry maid and laundry worker, in both domestic service and industry, it is likely that she would have kept abreast of changes in washing powders, technology and regulations governing work. She probably even teaches newcomers to her multinational laundry business, passing on up-to-date information.

One particular student had completed a coronary care course ten years earlier. She had worked in that speciality ever since that date and had taught students in both the classroom and practice settings. She had attended numerous study days, was a member of a coronary care nursing forum, helped develop the speciality curriculum and commissioned a new coronary care unit. It would be difficult to dispute the fact that she is up-to-date but, adhering to the letter of the APL law, the contribution of that original course to her present level of knowledge/skill is probably minimal in comparison to uncertificated and experiential learning which has built upon that original learning.

4. The context in which the claim is made

It is important to remember that prior learning cannot be recognised for APL purpose unless it is relevant to the claimant's intended course of study. Prior learning has to be **mapped** against something for APL purposes. Whether the university calls the credits recognised as prior learning **general or specific credit** (see *chapter 2*), the fact remains that either its general or specific **relevance** is being sought. The more information a claimant can provide the easier it is for an appropriate decision to be reached. Claimants may find that even a recently completed credit-rated course only receives a proportion of its full credit value because **only that portion of the learning is replicated within modules of the new course**. Therefore, unless the claimant realises this, s/he may be disappointed when presenting for APL a certificate that carries a credit value of, for example, 60 level two credits and it is recognised for only 20 level two credits. This is by no means saying that the course was not originally worth 60 credits, but only a third of its content is relevant in the context of the course s/he has chosen to study in the future.

Credit transfer tariff

In some instances it is possible for staff involved with a particular course to produce what is called a **credit-transfer tariff**. This task is usually undertaken when it is considered likely that a number of students will ask for APL in respect of the same certificates. If, for example, an institution developed a degree in care of the older adult, it is likely that a number of nurses coming forward for this course would seek APL in respect of ENB 298 (care of the older person). Members of the course team would consider, before any claimants presented a claim, how the learning covered within the ENB 298 course overlaps with learning offered within their newly developed degree programme. Once they have come to a decision about academic credit in respect of this course certificate, then each and every nurse presenting this certificate will see, on a list, the likely **number and level of credit** s/he will attain through APL. It is important to note that this number and level of academic credit for prior learning is not guaranteed because firstly, there are variations in breadth and depth of content of ENB 298 courses, despite the title being the same, and, secondly, some students may have completed the course before assessment was a requirement.

Presenting certificates for APL

Step 1

Once a claimant has obtained documents relating to the course s/he wishes to embark upon, s/he should consider the following:

1a. Is APL permitted and what rules and regulations apply?

The documents may, for example, say that prior learning may contribute only up to a certain number of credits or it may say that no prior learning can be considered in respect of certain compulsory modules.

1b. Is any of his/her prior certificated learning relevant to this course?

While the title of the intended award will give a guide as to which prior learning may be relevant, eg. BSc (Hons) Counselling, the claimant will find it more helpful to look at the syllabus, aims, objectives/ outcomes and content outline. If the course is modularised, module titles and their individual learning outcomes provide the best guide.

If s/he cannot find this information, or it is not clear within the written documents, s/he should contact the institution and ask to speak to someone who can give information about either the intended course or AP(E)L. It may be possible to arrange a meeting with a member of the academic or administrative staff but, at this stage, it is likely to be exploratory only. Claimants need to check whether there would be a fee for such a preliminary meeting.

Step 2

Once a claimant has decided that s/he has a worthwhile APL claim s/he should present the claim in whatever way the particular institution advises. It is most likely that s/he will be requested to:

2a. Complete an APL claim form.

2b. Present the original certificate.

The institute may permit a photocopy to be submitted but, at some point, the original must be shown.

Step 3

Claimants may be requested to provide supporting information/ documentary evidence.

3a.   If a course was awarded academic credit the claimant should provide any documentary evidence of this, assuming it is not already evident from the certificate.

Sometimes it is necessary to request a transcript from the previous course in order to get a statement of its credit value. Claimants should check if there is a fee for this service.

3b.   Unless the content of the previously completed course is totally clear from its title, claimants will need to provide the syllabus/ curriculum.

Failing this, they may prepare a brief summary of the content of the course. Even ENB numbered awards which share the same title (and minimum learning hours and outcomes) vary in content, depending upon the institution in which they are delivered. This is why the person responsible for APL will need as much relevant information as possible if s/he is to make an accurate APL recommendation.

3c.   If a claimant is attempting to APL against a specific module/s, ie. seeking specific credit, it may be helpful to use highlighter pens to show where the content/objectives/outcomes of his/her previous course map against that of the specific module/s in the intended course.

If, for example, a claimant is trying to show that prior learning maps against the outcomes of a module in the new course, s/he could use pink to highlight mapping words/phrases/sections within the syllabus, course content list, assignments etc. If s/he wants to show where the outcomes of a second module can be mapped, then highlight these sections in green and so on. This shows the claimant's analytical skills as well as ability to determine what is relevant from what isn't. These are important attributes for a student in higher education.

3d.   If a claim is particularly relevant to practice, the claimant may be required to present evidence that learning has been applied in current practice.

This is usually done through an essay, report or case/care study.

3e.   Provide information concerning the mode of attendance eg. full-time, part-time, distance learning, and both the start and finish date.

Two courses might have very similar aims and objectives but one course may last from 2 January to 1 February (31 days), with two x one week study blocks (ten days) during that period. Another course may start on 2 January and end on 31 October (304 days) but still only have ten study days during that time. This kind of information is essential if the person with responsibility for APL is to have all necessary information at his/her disposal.

3f. Provide information concerning the number of hours/days direct tuition (sometimes called contact hours) and an approximation of the number of hours spent in study, research, reading, ie. self-managed learning.

This latter element of a course can sometimes amount to two or three times the number of contact hours.

3g. It may be that the awarding body is known, by the institution, to require assessment in order to satisfy themselves that learning has taken place and not just attendance. Under these circumstances, the certificate alone gives sufficient evidence.

The APL adviser will be able to tell claimants whether their certificates alone are sufficient.

3h. If the certificate alone is insufficient evidence of assessment a claimant should provide information on the nature and topic of assessment, together with a sample of work, if retained.

3i If, at the time of completion, it was not explicitly stated (on certificate or transcript) the academic level of the course studied, a claimant may be asked to provide an example of assessed work. This is so the person with responsibility for APL can assure him/herself that, even though the prior learning is relevant in terms of subject/objectives, it is also of the relevant academic level.

3j. If, at the time of completion, academic credit was not yet awarded it may be necessary for the person with responsibility for APL to see a sample of written work, or to meet with the claimant to clarify the unstated level of his/her attainment.

Step 4

Where assessment did not take place, claimants will need to satisfy the institution that they did achieve the outcomes/objectives of the course leading to the certificate. If a claimant was not formally assessed in order to gain the prior certificate, or the institution has concerns regarding the academic level of previous studies, then s/he may be offered the opportunity to undertake some form of assessment, usually written but sometimes through interview. As previously mentioned, sometimes it takes the form of the assessment normally undertaken by those studying the module in question (challenge method) or that of a course similar to the one previously completed by the claimant. While this may seem onerous, it should not be too difficult if a claimant already has the knowledge and, under these circumstances, it is preferable (in terms of time, money and satisfaction) to repeating the learning.

Step 5: Show currency of learning

If a claimant's certificate is more than five years old s/he may be requested to present information on how knowledge/skills have been kept alive through, for example, study days, reading and experience. S/he may be asked to present this claim as an **uncertificated/ experiential learning claim** (APEL) rather than an APL claim with supporting documentation. Claimants should bear in mind that APEL may carry a different fee from APL and check the precise fee level for claiming certificated learning with supporting experiential evidence.

Questions and actions

1. Consider which course you wish to embark upon.
2. Obtain information pertaining to the course aims, objectives, content and outcomes.
3. Find out whether APL is permitted.
4. Find out how long it normally takes to process an APL claim and whether claimants must have received written confirmation of their APL credits prior to commencing a new course. This will tell you whether you can achieve APL credits within your timescale.
5. Find out how much APL would cost.
6. Ask about the arrangements and regulations regarding APL.
7. Consider whether you can identify a match between your prior certificated learning and that of the new course.
8. Express your interest in making an APL claim to the institution.
9. Follow the advice given in written leaflets or forms. Support your claim with as much information as possible (see *steps 2 and 3* above).
10. If your prior learning requires support from experiential learning and subsequent education, find out if this carries a different fee.

Chapter 5
Making an experiential learning claim

Summary box

1. Assessment/accreditation of prior experiential learning (APEL) normally refers to learning that has been acquired through attendance at **short courses/study days, through reading and/or experience**. This learning has not previously been presented for academic assessment.

2. Experiential learning can only be submitted for assessment and accreditation if it is relevant within the context of a particular course leading to an award. It may be acceptable if it is relevant to the overall themes of the award or it may be required to match specific elements of the award.

3. Claimants are responsible for mapping their prior learning against their chosen course and for providing sufficient range, breadth and depth of evidence to assure their assessor of the legitimacy of the claim. The learning must be equivalent to that achieved via the taught (traditional) route.

4. EL evidence is normally supported by a written explanatory commentary that links/cross-references individual items of evidence with themes or specific outcomes within the intended course.

5. The assessor is concerned with both the **knowledge base underpinning practice** and the way in which such knowledge has been **applied and modified** and new knowledge generated through practice.

Experience

Experience is what happens to us. However, simply having an experience does not mean that we learn from it. We undergo various experiences, sometimes at our choosing but, at other times, they just happen. We are unlikely to choose to have a road traffic accident but these things happen. During experiences we observe the situation and the reactions of ourselves and others. Sometimes we are told what to do in a given situation and we evaluate the quality of such instruction. Some of this data input and processing (usually called thinking) may take place without us realising that it is happening, but to turn experience into experiential learning there is a need for more systematic and conscious thinking.

What is experiential learning?

Learning is the process of gaining knowledge and is maximised when we make a conscious effort to gain knowledge. We can watch and listen to someone who is cooking a particular dish... that's an experience. However, we might decide that we want to cook that same dish for our weekend guests and so, rather than just undergoing the experience, we pay attention to what the demonstrator says, watch carefully how s/he prepares it and make a note of the ingredients. This is a conscious intention to gain knowledge rather than to let an opportunity stay at the experience stage.

The demonstrator transmits to us **knowledge and insights,** saving us considerable time and effort. We know, for example, what is likely to be the result if we do what s/he has done. The trouble is, it always looks so easy when the demonstrator does it. When it comes to the weekend, it may be that we don't follow the instructions exactly as given in the demonstration. We might, for example, have two small tins rather than the one large one that the demonstrator suggested and decide to use what we have rather than spend additional money. We might leave the dish in the oven for the amount of time that the demonstrator suggested but, when we look at it, we don't think it is cooked enough for our guests' taste and so decide to leave it in for another ten minutes. After all this, when it comes to eating it, we might consider that it is too sharp or too salty and make a mental note (or even a written one) that, next time, we will modify the ingredients in a particular way. What has happened is that we have achieved **a greater degree of knowledge and insight as a result of our experience**.

Reflection

When we reflect, we think back over some event or situation. In the example above, we made a conscious decision to learn through experience and, if we didn't reflect upon the experience, we would simply reproduce the same, overly salty dish, on the next occasion, and the next and so on. In this example, we have not merely let our learning stay at the '**given knowledge**' stage because we have applied it and modified it in the light of experience. We might decide that although the dish was good, and would be especially good if we used less salt or it was rather expensive and time-consuming and, to be honest, the shop-bought version is cheaper, more convenient, and just as good.

Through nursing and midwifery education we are continually **receiving knowledge** based upon the insights and research of others. But, as we know all too well, sometimes this wisdom sits comfortably in the world of our own practice, while, at other times, we might say, 'that's not what's meant to happen' or 'that won't work in my department'. In these circumstances, hopefully, we don't just discard the **theory**, we look at what fits and what doesn't, why and what modifications need to be made in this situation. We think (reflect) logically and systematically about it. It is as if someone is holding up a mirror for us. We ask ourselves, 'why didn't it work as it was meant to, what was different this time', and so on. If we don't ask these questions we are wasting a learning opportunity. If we don't have time to ask these questions when the event is taking place, we need to ask them later.

The Experiential Learning Cycle

Kolb and Fry (1975) talked about an **experiential learning cycle** in which participants tried to make sense of an experience in the light of previous experiences and knowledge. They looked for relationships between the known past and the novel present. They looked for similarities and differences between the present experience and those of the past and tried to explain what was happening through knowledge that they had already gained. Sometimes past knowledge was relevant, sometimes it only made partial sense or was only partly right, and sometimes it didn't fit at all. They queried why? As a result, the participants gained new insights (knowledge). This, in turn, was added to their existing 'personal encyclopaedia' for use in the future.

Sometimes we get little opportunity to reflect during an experience because we are running from one situation to another with little room for conscious reflection. However, if we never reflect upon that experience then, the chances are, we will fail to learn from it. Imagine carrying out a procedure and finding that it goes badly wrong but, instead of reflecting on why, the procedure is repeated in exactly the same way on the next occasion. When the patient cries out in pain, I don't think s/he would get much consolation from a response such as, 'Funny that, every time I do this my patients scream'.

Making the most of an experience

Reflection is a mental process. We reflect by:

i)   noticing the **circumstances and context** in which an event is taking place

ii)   analysing **who** is involved and the part that all participants, whether present or absent, are playing (one doesn't have to be in the immediate vicinity to be a key player, eg. a relative of a hospitalised patient)

iii) considering what is meant to happen, what theory tells us this and what assumptions this is based upon

iv)   comparing this with what is happening

v)   working out why things are happening (including emotions)

vi)   sifting out what is going well from what could be better

vii) widening the context to include **environmental, social, cultural, political, legal, ethical, gender, professional, organisational considerations**

viii) recollecting how any/all of the above fit in with information/knowledge/theory gained from books, journals, lectures, research findings etc

ix)   teasing out what can be learned from this experience

x)   planning what might be done next time and why.

Out of the experience has come new knowledge and insights. Some of this is old (we read about it or were taught by others) but some is modified/added to/new knowledge and insights.

We have just applied theory to practice and generated theory from practice.

Academic credit

Both the **old and the new knowledge and insights** are what academic credit is about. Academic credit is not really interested in whether the claimant can give an injection (unless the academic happens to be on the receiving end of the needle). It is interested in what the claimant knows that causes him/her to give the injection in that way, eg. your knowledge of body tissues, nerve pathways, pharmacology, microbiology, social psychology, ethicolegal matters etc. I could probably train a monkey to go through the mechanics of giving an injection, but what about the knowledge? At what point would my well-trained baboon come unstuck — or rather, when would his/her patient suffer as a result of the lack of knowledge?

I find the whole area of reflection a fascinating subject. If you want to read more about this I would suggest you try Boud *et al* (1985) or Reed and Proctor (1993).

Getting the knowledge to start with

We have considered the process of accrediting prior certificated learning in *chapter 4*. Information, insights, knowledge and theory (call it what you like) comes to us via **tuition**, **reading**, **practice** and, some might argue, **intuition**. In the case of tuition and reading, this is **pre-existing knowledge**. It has been recorded, usually in print. Someone has carried out some research and recorded his/her findings for the benefit of others. This enables those findings (just like this book) to sit on a shelf and to be available to a large number of people for many years. At some point the knowledge will become dated and, at that point, the information will be of more historical relevance. Writing down knowledge is a very efficient means of transmitting information because, but for this, each one of us would need to work everything out for ourselves.

Imagine what it would be like if every nurse had to open up several patients to discover how the stomach worked or cause their patients and relatives different degrees of suffering in order to follow a pain pathway or note psychological reactions. Once we can read, we have a vast amount of knowledge at our fingertips.

Doing the business

However, in nursing and midwifery, we are a **practice rich profession**. We don't just learn the ingredients and the way to make the dish — we do something with that knowledge. Our information, insights, knowledge, and theories cannot be fully realised unless we are able to apply them in practice and, just as we modified our cookery, modify and add to them in the light of our findings. We all know how the cake is supposed to rise, but why didn't it on this occasion? Maybe there will be/have been other occasions when it hasn't risen... What do they have in common... How does that change our knowledge base? Anyway, who says a cake has to rise... Does it taste just as good, or even better, if it doesn't rise? The assumption is that a risen cake tastes and looks better, but why?

Challenging assumptions in our practice

Challenging assumptions is an important part of academic life. At one time, the assumption was that the earth was flat and, if one went to the edge and kept going, one would fall off. In our profession we used to live with the assumption that if you put an unspecified amount of salt in the patient's bath his/her wounds healed more quickly. Who told us this? What were their findings based upon? Did we check on the validity and reliability of this information or did we just accept it as fact? As a student nurse, I am ashamed to admit that I made the salt manufacturers very rich. I don't remember wondering if my patients' wounds would have healed just as well if I poured washing-up liquid into their baths. I did ask why it was that one Sister told me to put oxygen and honey on a pressure sore, while another insisted I put oxygen and egg-white. The response I received was not very encouraging to one who sought a good final report and so I tried to work it out in my own mind. I decided that oxygen had something to do with fighting off anaerobic bacteria, while honey was energy for the commensals and egg-white was protein to create new tissue. Basically, my rationale was a load of rubbish and the true answer was that each Sister had learned to do it that way from another Sister and so on. Nowadays, I'd want to see the research reports, the controlled trials and make my own wound healing measurements before I could be convinced.

At the moment, we are encouraged to consider early discharge from hospital as a good thing. We are told that cross-infection is less likely and that patients do better in their own surroundings. However, I would ask you to consider:

i) what evidence is this based upon
ii) is it always the case that early discharge is best
iii) if we believe early discharge is best, what alternatives does it stop us exploring
iv) what ulterior motives might there be in fostering a belief in the value of early discharge
v) who stands to benefit from early discharge, besides a patient who avoids cross-infection
vi) what is the down-side of early discharge and what are the adverse consequences?

Professional progress

For us, because the real world of practice is unpredictable, each situation has an element of uniqueness, very little is clear-cut, and every patient is different. No knowledge is worth much unless it has transfer value but, because every situation in nursing and midwifery is full of variables, we can't just tranfer it without thought and modification. When we first enter the profession we tend to imitate others. We follow rules and react to what is happening. We can deal with simple, single problems, particularly when they have a limited number of possible solutions. As we gain in knowledge and confidence we become more independent and proactive. We also begin to break the rules when we can see that, while the principles apply, the precise ways in which things are normally done are not relevant in every situation. We become skilled in dealing with complex problems, all at the same time, and in situations where there are any number of possible solutions, each with a number of possible consequences. We could never move from this novice state to our present state without learning (Benner, 1984). It is not surprising, therefore, that nurses and midwives, with such a wealth of insight, knowledge and theoretical understanding underpinning their practice, are among the professional groups making greatest use of APEL.

Accreditation of prior experiential learning

Experiential learning, in respect of APEL, is any learning that has not resulted from a course leading to testamentary evidence of achievement, eg. a certificate. The term encompasses learning attained through courses for which there was no assessment, short courses, study days, in-service training and learning gained through practical experiences.

In addition, as we have seen in *chapters 2 and 3*, holders of certificates five or more years old may be asked to support their certificated learning claim with evidence of updating through subsequent uncertificated and experiential learning.

An experiential learning claim

Claimants are required to identify experiential learning that is **relevant in the context of the course they intend to pursue**. Relevance requires the learning to be either:
1. Relevant to the general themes and title of the award gained from the intended course of study, or
2. Equivalent to the outcomes of specific modules within the intended course. These are usually compulsory modules.

1. Learning may be relevant to the general themes and title of the award gained from the intended course of study

Experiential learning may be accepted as an **integral part of a course**, for example in place of optional/elective modules, or as a means of attaining the number of credits required to embark upon a top-up degree, eg. a top-up degree intended for nurses and midwives who already hold a diploma in higher education. Without the opportunity to use AP(E)L, those who do not hold such an academic award would be ineligible for the top-up degree. Through a combination of APL and APEL a number of nurses and midwives register for these courses, particularly in the area of community studies.

> Claimant A: A group of qualified nurses and midwives attended an information session on a top-up degree. At first, there were a lot of long faces because few of those in the room held the entry requirement of Dip HE. It was explained that, as an alternative to this certificate, a nurse or midwife could submit an AP(E)L claim. Then, one potential student put it in the following way. 'It's as if I'm being asked to show that I've got the same, or more, knowledge than a nurse who has just graduated off a Dip HE course. I certainly know I have — it's just a question of putting it in writing.' Because this was said in the presence of others the effect was to give them all an added confidence boost! What they remained worried about was providing sufficient evidence of their knowledge. We cannot assume a nurse/midwife with 20 years experience knows more than a Project 2000 graduate, nor that she is as up-to-date. It has to be shown/evidenced.

One of the difficulties of claims where the claimant is attempting to show the general relevance of prior experiential learning rather than a match to existing modules, is that s/he has to write his/her own learning outcomes. These outcomes must reflect the **academic level of learning** For example, compare the following two examples of written outcomes:

a) 'I can help patients develop the skills needed to self-medicate.'

b) 'I can construct individualised self-medication programmes.'

In the former outcome the claimant has not made it clear whether or not s/he designed the programme, whereas it is clear from the second outcome that the claimant has the knowledge him/herself to devise and modify programmes based upon individual needs.

2. Learning may be equivalent to the outcomes of specific modules within the intended course. These are usually compulsory modules

Although the claimant may be required to match prior learning to the existing outcomes of specific modules, the advantage is that the outcomes have already been written and, therefore, the claimant does not have to grapple with the thorny issue of ensuring that the written outcome reflects the academic level of learning — someone else has already done that.

Combining certificated and experiential learning

It is important to remember that claimants cannot make an experiential learning claim for learning that has already been accredited through the process of APL. For example, a nurse may hold a certificate in care of the elderly which may be recognised for a certain number of credits. Any claim in relation to experiential learning in the field of elderly care must avoid any overlap because, in effect, double credit is being given for the same learning. This is yet another example of what is called **double-counting**. However, if the nurse's claim relates to an aspect of elderly care that was not encompassed within the certificated learning or she has significantly built upon the initial learning attained through the certificate (and already recognised through APL) then this would constitute a legitimate APEL claim. If the experiential learning claimed is at a higher academic level than that recognised for the certificate then this would also be legitimate.

As already mentioned, claimants who wish to receive accreditation for certificated learning deemed to be potentially out-of-date may be asked to **support their claim by showing how experience and education updating has maintained the currency of the learning**. For example, an ENB 998 completed six years ago may be supported by reference to the duty rota showing mentorship of students over a period of time, assessment documents completed by the claimant, teaching sessions presented, education audit reports, tape-recorded teaching sessions, letters of attendance at teaching and assessing related events etc.

Those members of academic staff who grapple with AP(E)L frequently have to make decisions about the legitimacy of an experiential learning claim. Fortunately, the full complexity of these decisions doesn't need to be elaborated upon in this book but, suffice to say, decisions are rarely, if ever, made in a cavalier fashion, as you will see when we look at the process of an APEL claim.

The APEL process

Step 1: Initial feasibility study

Before claimants can decide whether they have an APEL claim they need to:
i)   decide which course they intend to study
ii) consider how prior experiential and uncertificated learning map against the themes and outcomes of the intended course
iii) find out what the AP(E)L rules and regulations are and whether they would be permitted to make a claim relating to general relevance to the course themes and award title, whether they must match specific module outcomes, or whether a combination of both is permitted
iv) find out how much an APEL claim will cost and what support they can expect
v)   consider what impact an AP(E)L claim will have on their studies (see *chapter 2*)
vi) find out how long processing the claim is likely to take from the date of submission. This is particularly important if the claimant is required to have attained a certain number of credits prior to commencing their chosen course or where a module s/he is hoping to gain exemption from occurs at the beginning of the course.

Some of this information will be found in course and AP(E)L literature but it may be helpful to seek an appointment with an AP(E)L adviser or co-ordinator. There may be a charge for such a meeting. Generally, it is easier, and often cheaper, to make a claim in respect of certificated learning and, therefore, it is very wise to ascertain how much credit could be attained through APL, and what aspects of the intended course this would cover, before embarking upon the more lengthy process of APEL.

Step 2: Linking with an adviser

Claimants are normally linked to an APEL adviser who will facilitate their claim. The adviser can offer advice on how to identify relevant learning, how to think analytically and reflect upon learning, and how to present a claim. S/he can provide insight into the criteria against which a claim will be judged. Sometimes this support is offered in the form of a group session/s.

It is for the claimant to identify his/her learning and to present the claim, not the APEL adviser. As an adviser myself, I never told a claimant that his/her portfolio would 'pass' (gain the credits sought). This decision is for an APEL assessor and, as previously mentioned, it is good practice to ensure that the adviser and the assessor are not one-and-the-same for any one claimant. If I was assessing a claim, I made sure that I was not involved in giving advice. I did, however, offer advice to claimants on where I thought their work was strong or weak and how it could be improved. I normally told them when the claim was at a point where I considered it worthwhile to submit it while emphasising that I could not be an expert in every subject or course and could not, therefore, give the kind of informed judgement a carefully selected assessor could give. This kind of facilitation is no different from that which a student receives from the module leader when presenting work in respect of more traditional assessments. You wouldn't expect the module leader to provide so much input to one student's essay that, in effect, s/he was marking his/her own work. Unless s/he did this for every student it would be extremely unfair on those who didn't get this patronage. At the end of the course, the tutor might as well write his/her own name on the certificate. There are many similarities between the assessment of prior experiential learning and more 'traditional' assessments, and this is quite right. APEL is just another form of assessment, no more or less rigorous and no more or less credible.

Step 3: Identifying learning for academic recognition

We saw in *chapter 3* how Charlotte teased out the learning from her experience. In particular, we saw how she identified learning resulting from her experiences in social skills training (SST) and assertiveness training (AT). It is important that claimants do justice to their knowledge and skills through writing learning outcomes that reflect its true depth and academic level.**The claimant is required to identify the number of credits being claimed and at which level.**

Academic level 1

The student is expected to understand broad principles in relation to the specific area of study. S/he is expected to retain given information and apply it to specific situations or use it to solve relatively straightforward problems. Learning outcomes might use verbs such as: describe, explain, identify, appreciate, extract, select, and utilise.

Academic level 2

The student is expected to have a more in-depth understanding of a number of concepts and theories in relation to a broader area of study.

S/he is expected to be able to make connections between related theory and practice and propose reasons for discrepencies. S/he would be expected to apply the knowledge to a variety of situations and use it to solve more complex problems, but where there are a relatively limited number of choices and consequences. Learning outcomes might use verbs such as: interpret, apply, criticise, analyse, collate, predict.

Academic level 3

By this stage, the student is expected to have a broader and deeper knowledge base, having read around subjects. S/he would be expected to be able to critically analyse competing theories, to determine their validity in a range of situations and to formulate convincing, well-reasoned, arguments. Learning outcomes might use verbs such as: critically analyse, probe, discriminate, formulate, evaluate, construct, organise, create.

Unfortunately, all institutions do not agree over the precise definition of the different levels. When claimants are given guidance on the criteria used in assessments (and in considering APEL claims) they should be able to see how their chosen institution differentiates one academic level from another.

Step 4: Gather evidence of learning

Just as we saw in *chapter 4* how an APL claimant had to gather evidence, eg. certificate and other documents, so it is necessary for the APEL claimant to **provide evidence of experiential learning**. Evidence can take an enormous variety of forms. Evidence, as it suggests in court, is proof that something has occured; in this case, learning. If, for example, a claimant was evidencing that s/he could travel on public transport, possible evidence would be a number of used bus and train tickets showing journeys of varying lengths, a photograph of him/herself at a bus stop, on a main line station and a tube station and a written statement from members of London transport and British Rail staff. The kinds of evidence nurses and midwives present in support of APEL claims include: care plans, testimonials, care studies, committee minutes, policy documents, diary notes, tape recordings, videos, teaching packages, patient information leaflets, annotated bibliographies, lecture notes, letters, articles, confirmation of attendance at study days/short courses, appraisals, photographs and proposals.

All evidence must be authentic and be clearly explained in relation to the claimants involvement with it. For example, a policy may be submitted because the claimant was instrumental in its drafting and this may be supported by committee minutes. However, a policy drafted by others may still be a legitimate piece of evidence, eg. it might illustrate a particular point, but the claimant should make clear that it is not his/her work.

At times, there is so little hard evidence to present in respect of a 'soft' skill, eg. developing therapeutic relationships, that an essay, specifically written for the purpose, is one of the few means of evidencing attainment of an outcome. This is as legitimate, in my view, as writing a care study to evidence learning, but others may not share my view. Experiential learning is about practice and, so long as the essay is **practice oriented and relates to the underpinning knowledge (old or new) that informs practice** I can see no objection to this. Purists will say that the fact that you can write, in an essay, about the way that something should be done is no guarantee that you do it in practice. This can be countered by providing evidence of activities relevant to the subject of the essay, as well as citing specific examples of practice in the essay. Wherever possible, claimants should provide a sufficient range and quantity of evidence rather than just one item. Evidence of experiential learning is just as prone to the 'past its sell-by date' phenomenon as is certificated learning. If, for example, a claimant presents a teaching package developed five years ago I, as the assessor, would want to know whether it is still appropriate, has s/he modified it in the light of experience or new knowledge and, if s/he were rewriting it today, how would it be changed and why? The claimant should not wait for me to ask these questions — s/he should answer them for the assessor in the explanatory notes accompanying such evidence (see below).

Obviously, claimants should remove all reference to patient, staff or hospital names. Claimants may be asked to remove all reference to their own name. This is a little difficult when it comes to including a testimonial from your manager.

Let's get away from nursing/midwifery for a moment and imagine that I have decided to present a claim for accreditation of experiential learning against a module called 'Washing clothing'. As evidence, I might submit:

- photographs of me doing the washing by hand and machine
- photographs of washing before and after
- a written testimony from those for whom I wash clothing
- a tape-recording of me talking through the process of washing by hand and machine
- a video of me teaching my teenage son (if I had one) how to wash his own clothing.

However, the outcomes of this fictitious module must be uppermost in my mind. If, for example, it requires me to 'Explain the biochemical reactions of a range of washing products' then I will need to show that I am aware of the full range of products, eg. biological, detergent and have sufficient background knowledge of biochemistry to know about emulsifying agents and biological degradation. I may find it harder to come up with evidence of this knowledge and need to write an essay on the topic or include it as an integral part of my supporting commentary, eg. talking about research in relation to dermatological reactions when hand-washing using biological detergent. If I have done a lot of reading about different washing powders and their reactions, I might decide to present, as evidence, what is called an annotated bibliography. For this, I would provide a list of those articles and books that I had read (just as the reference/bibliography at the back of a book), but I would write a few lines about the contents of the article or book and how it informs my judgement.

As you can see, the more carefully selected evidence I present, the more convincing my case for credit.

Back to nursing/midwifery now. If a nurse/midwife was claiming prior learning equivalent to a module outcome which expected students to be able to 'Present information on HIV/AIDS to a mixed recipient group' s/he might choose to present her lecture notes and handouts from a talk given to students of nursing and midwifery, notes from a talk given to members of the general public and a third set from a talk given to HIV sufferers. The supporting commentary would explain the differences, highlight particular points with regard to terminology, provide the rationale for choice of venue, language, dress and elaborate on the purpose for the talks.

Step 5: Cross-referencing evidence with learning outcomes

Claimants cannot expect to submit evidence without any explanation of how each item of evidence (artefact) relates to the learning outcomes being claimed. The claimant is endeavouring to direct the assessor to those elements of his/her APEL portfolio that have been mapped against elements of the course s/he intends to pursue and, having done this, to convince the assessor that these elements are sufficiently equivalent to warrant recognition of prior learning. That reads as quite a mouthful — what it means is that claimants need to take the assessor by the hand and say 'look at this section and compare it with this part of the course. As you can see, i) the prior learning is very relevant to this award, ii) the two are identical'.

Perhaps the hardest part of an APEL claim is supporting the evidence with a written commentary that:

1. Sets the scene

Claimants should set the scene by telling the assessor the context in which the learning took place or how the opportunity arose to achieve those outcomes. Identify the process that took place. For example, a claimant might begin by saying something like:

' i) I intend to satisfy my assessor that I have met the following learning outcomes. List the outcomes.

ii) I had the opportunity to achieve this learning through.... Insert the title of short courses/study days, specific reading, roles and experiences that created the opportunities.

iii) The learning took place between... Insert relevant dates.

iv) I have provided as evidence... List the individual artefacts that have been included, giving each a number.

v) I have provided a supporting commentary that will:

  i) link each artefact to relevant outcome/s

  ii) provide explanation

  iii) offer further insight into the authenticity of my claim.'

This logical introduction suggests that the claimant is confident in his/her knowledge and promises a well organised APEL portfolio.

2. Explains how each item of evidence put forward relates to one or more outcomes claimed

Claimant B: One claimant was attempting to evidence a match between prior learning and the outcomes of a module covering care planning. As evidence, she submitted two care plans. While they were well written, though not extensive, I, as assessor, could only infer or assume that she had been aware of the model that appeared to have been used, that she was aware of the process of individualised care, and that there was good justification for the plan and decisions made. What I needed was a supporting commentary to accompany the care plans. This commentary should anticipate all the questions I might ask when trying to assure myself that the claimant has achieved the outcome she claims. It should talk me through each outcome and link each piece of evidence with the outcome it supports. The module in question had six learning outcomes: was I supposed to assume both the care plans evidenced achievement of each and every outcome, or did some parts relate to some outcomes? It isn't up to me to guess!

3. Provides the assessor with further insight into the academic level of attainment

Commentaries are informative when they are liberally scattered with words and phrases such as:

because... , if... , unless... , however... , for example... , this is illustrated by... , thinking back on this... , I now know that... , I realised that... , I learned... , the assumption was... , the alternatives were... , the consequences might have been... , this proved... , and so....

Such words tend to answer the questions an assessor would ask. For example, if I were to read that the patient was placed in the supine position my first question would be 'Does the nurse/midwife know why?' It may be right to place him/her in that position but the fact that it was done could have been more luck than judgement. When writing about anything that has been done:

i) explain statements made and give the rationale for decisions, eg. 'I say this because... '

ii) provide examples that support what is being said (I call these illuminating examples because they 'light up' the text)

iii) offer insight into the criteria being used when a judgement has been made

iv) provide comparisons

v) show leadership, expertise, innovation, self-direction and creativity.

This is similar to when we have had a very questioning student nurse/midwife allocated to us and how everything has to be explained and supported, since everything is challenged. Hopefully, the student goes away with the feeling that s/he has benefited from being allocated to a knowledgeable practitioner, rather than just spending ten or twelve weeks 'serving time'.

Remember, the assessor is looking for evidence that you have relevant learning or have matched specific outcomes. In a class-room setting, when students are being assessed, they are expected to have acquired background/underpinning knowledge and to process this and apply it in a manner that reflects the academic level (see academic levels above). They are required to show not just achievement of the module outcomes but to evidence their ability to write in an academic style, to show they can gather and collate materials, and to show the development of an analytical, challenging, and reflective style. APEL claimants need to show the same characteristics as taught students.

Step 6: Collating all materials into an APEL portfolio

An APEL portfolio is normally a ring binder with dividers and an index. Claimants do not endear themselves to assessors if the assessor is left to rummage around, trying to find bits of evidence that are referred to at various points; nor does it show the abilities that suggest the claimant is capable of selecting, collating and organising, all of which are essential skills in a graduate. Colour coding, numbering or any other means of cross-referencing is invaluable. Sometimes two binders are used, evidence being provided in one and commentary in another. One item of evidence can support more than one outcome. These outcomes may even be contained within different modules if the claimant is attempting to match specific modules. Therefore, well thought out cross-referencing and indexing is essential.

Claimants are normally advised to submit their work at an agreed time and place and to obtain some form of confirmation that it has been handed in, eg. a written receipt. When submitting most types of course work for assessment purposes it is normal, as well as sensible, to retain a copy for oneself. Sometimes students are required to submit two or even three copies. This is difficult in the case of an APEL portfolio because of the nature and volume of evidence and supporting commentary. However, by handing the file in yourself, and getting a receipt, you can eliminate some of the problems associated with postal delivery in a large organisation. Be very careful if you are submitting any document that could not be duplicated, unless you photocopy it first. Ask before you submit an original certificate since, within the portfolio, a photocopy may suffice, together with a signed statement that your APEL adviser has seen the original.

Step 7: Assessment

Any claim is likely to be assessed by a member of academic staff with knowledge of the subject area claimed as prior knowledge and with a knowledge of the course against which the learning is being mapped. This person should have had some staff development with regard to AP(E)L and may be acting as an APEL adviser to other students. They should use institutionally agreed criteria to formulate recommendations. Claimants may be offered the opportunity to support their written portfolio with a viva (an oral examination). Sometimes two or even three people are involved in the decision making process. They may then be required to place their recommendations in respect of each claim before a committee convened to consider all APEL claims. To eliminate possible bias, a claimant's APEL adviser will not normally be permitted to make the decision.

Step 8: Notification of results

How long claimants have to wait for a final decision depends upon the assessment cycle. If, for example, you submit your claim just after an assessment board has met then you will be delayed by the need to wait for the next board. However, you may be given what is called an unratified result in the meantime. Results are usually given in writing and you may or may not have your AP(E)L portfolio returned to you. The safest and cheapest method is to collect it at an agreed time and place.

Theory	Practice
Level one	
Takes in, retains and recalls given information. Understands principles. Makes connections.	Takes lead from others. Follows rules. Selects out and imitates appropriate behaviours. Recognises inconsistencies. Solves simple problems using reasoning. Describes events using salient points. Supervised safe performance. Applies theory to practice.
Level two	
Gathers and sifts data from a wide range of sources. Proposes reasons for discrepencies and ambiguities. Judges validity of perspectives. Recognises flaws in own argument.	Explores events and constructs possible explanations. Autonomous in familiar situations. Solves problems in which there are various options and consequences. Makes reasoned decisions using limited data. Safe/skilled in a range of activities. Adapts theory to practice.
Level three	
Critically analyses competing theories. Argues, refutes, supports. Validates own theories. Unravels complex problems, predicts consequences and evaluates options. Generates new data.	Leads, teaches, guides. Self-directing. Responds rapidly to minimal cues. Critically examines rules and roles. Anticipates events. Innovates practice. Highly skilled in specific areas. Resolves highly complex, multifaceted problems. Evaluates performance. Generates theory from practice.

Figure 5.1: Considering professional progress beside academic levels

Chapter 6
Examples of AP(E)L

This chapter is divided into two sections. In the first I have reproduced some past claimants comments about APEL. There is a lot of common ground with respect to what they found helpful, stressful and rewarding. Part-time education (most APEL claims are developed via this mode) can be a very lonely process. When the experience is a new one and the nature of the work is different from anything you are familiar with, it can seem that you are the only person experiencing the 'emotional labour of learning'. In the second section I have provided extracts from APEL claims to illustrate particular points.

Section 1: The experience of APEL

Claimant A: (A senior nurse in mental health care who found that his employers would only fund him for a top-up degree and, despite a number of years of experience, had few 'paper' qualifications.)

> 'I was interviewed and began the process of putting together my APEL portfolio. I was quite daunted because of the number of credits I had to achieve. I was not prepared for the amount of work necessary, but I wanted to do a degree and was motivated to complete my APEL. One of the most difficult aspects was trying to find evidence to support learning outcomes through clinical experience. I would advise anyone wishing to undertake APEL to keep any and all information relating to anything they have been involved in, in a safe and accessible place. Although it was hard to undertake such an extensive self-directed module, I felt that I had achieved something positive at the end of it and that my experience and prior learning had counted for something and was officially recognised.'

Claimant B: (A ward manager)

> 'My initial interest in AP(E)L was raised following a talk from our ward link tutor on the subject. I had previously felt that attaining a degree was completely out of my reach due to time constraints and never having studied at degree level. Spurred on by the support of a colleague, we decided to investigate what credits we may be able to build up with AP(E)L. I left the first session of the AP(E)L module both motivated but confused. I think it was at least the fourth or fifth week before I realised what exactly I had to prove within the portfolio. It was certainly more time consuming and difficult to justify my prior learning

and experience than I had expected, especially as many of the courses had been undertaken prior to credit ratings existing. I felt a great sense of achievement when I was awarded the maximum credit. Through AP(E)L I have been able to complete a degree without replicating learning and at a decreased cost to both myself and my manager.'

Claimant C: (A very senior nurse [30 years experience] with a national reputation and an important teaching role, describing the value of peer support.)

'This was valuable in that we were able to support each other. We also had the guidance of the APEL co-ordinator in providing us with the style of portfolio and the type of evidence required as well as giving us enough 'rope' to almost hang ourselves. We found this most reassuring and it was surprising how important this guidance became. It was useful to discuss our portfolios together. We needed to test out with each other regarding the credits we were hoping to gain. The danger is trying to claim too many credits and this is where the peer group can be useful in sharing information and ideas. The material was everywhere, in the office, at home, in drawers and filing cabinets. It is difficult to assess how much credence to give your work in terms of credits.'

(The same claimant describing feelings.)

'APEL is not an easy option. It requires many hours of thought, work and organisational ability. Feelings fluctuate from enthusiasm to "let's have a go", "why should I", "I'm giving up", "I have managed without a degree so far", "why not". All of these thoughts go through your mind. Waiting for the result of this (APEL claim) was a very anxious time, and seemed endless. It was an exciting moment when I learned that all was well, more exciting than having the award later. It felt really worth all the struggle and stress engendered.'

Claimant D: (A midwife with 20 years experience describing evidence gathering for an extensive [and impressive] APEL claim.)

'I turned my drawers inside out for notes from the courses that I had attended, reading and analysing them for meaningful solutions for module matching. I also had a deadline to keep. Would I be able to do it I kept asking myself? How about my day job, was I giving it my full potential? Writing up critical incidents was another big problem. This is another new approach to support my claim. I knew I had to compose in such a fashion that it was interesting and easily understood by any lay reader. After three consultations and discussions with (name of adviser) the portfolio was finally handed in. There was a sense of relief to know I had completed the hard work for APEL. I felt I had given my best and there was nothing else to give. My brain felt very empty. All I could do at this stage was wait.'

Claimant E: (An experienced specialist nurse describing the start of APEL and its additional benefits.)

'I had reached a stage in my career and professional development where I felt I needed and wanted to follow a degree course in Health Studies. I was encouraged to think that my 13 years post-registration experience and possession of ENB courses might "count for something". I was aware from the start that it was my responsibility to complete the portfolio, that it would involve looking at my experience and teasing out what was relevant, analysing what I had learnt and what evidence I could supply to support my commentary. But how could this "wealth of experience" be translated into academic credit? I was, at first, a little daunted by the process and somewhat ignorant of the university structure, but I was determined to make a go of it; after all, I had nothing to lose and I might even learn something in the process.

I found the introductory session about structure of university courses, eg. levels of credit and module structure, very helpful in filling in the gaps in my knowledge. The accompanying APEL guide was very helpful in reinforcing this information and giving clear guidance as to how to structure the portfolio. We also received plenty of encouragement and advice from the APEL co-ordinator. At the time of the APEL course I was also applying for two jobs so I found the time spent on reflection helped in my applications and subsequent interview preparation. The dates for submitting the draft portfolio helped me to discipline my time and complete the sections on time.

I feel that this experience will be useful in the future when I start my degree programme. I felt a great sense of achievement upon completing my submission; also at a loss as to what do do with my free time! I had learnt to reflect on my experience in a different light, not just what I had done but how my learning had fitted together and the steps involved. I gained valuable insight into completing academic work and also guidance in preparing to study again after a prolonged time.'

(The same nurse talking about peer support.)

'At this stage of the course (APEL module) I appreciated being able to talk to two other students on the course and compare notes. Not only were we able to share ideas but also identify areas in each other's portfolios that could be developed. Unfortunately, due to the pressures of other commitments we lost contact.'

Claimant F: (A ward manager who had no alternative but to use the distance learning approach and, therefore, had little contact with other students to support her.)

'At the time, I had no previous knowledge of what APEL was or what it involved. I had a vague notion it was an "extension" of my curriculum vitae. I did not initially appreciate the depth of work involved. Once I had been briefed about the requirements, I felt anxious and apprehensive about my ability to fulfil them. This made me think and rethink about whether I had made the correct decision to undertake a degree and wonder if perhaps I was trying to attain something I was not capable of. Once I had decided I had nothing to lose in attempting to produce an "analytical" piece of work, and started production, I began to feel more positive about my personal study skills. I found the one-to-one discussions with my APEL co-ordinator invaluable, not only to ensure I was providing the appropriate information at the necessary level, but also as encouragement and support. I did APEL through a distance learning package due to personal circumstances, and this negated the benefits of working in a group. I had the opportunity to see another submission and to observe how the work had been organised. This was of more benefit to me than the explanations in the booklets provided for APEL. I found APEL a daunting experience but valuable. It helped me to analyse my clinical and theoretical knowledge in an orderly manner. It was also a good introduction to degree courses. This gave me confidence when commencing my degree course, having had work accepted as proof I could write at an appropriate level.'

Claimant G: (A midwife with many years experience but, on paper, minimum qualifications.)

'I attended my first APEL study day with both apprehension and inquisitiveness. The day was packed with information — too much for me to take in at once — and I felt confusion and dismay at the end of the day. I also admit to feeling very disadvantaged as I had no ENB courses "tucked away" unlike most of the others. I realised that I had a very hard task ahead of me if I was to be successful. Over the next few days I quickly acknowledged my wealth of experience, then an absolute explosion of ideas, but tremendous apprehension as to how to "present" my experience in the APEL process. Over the weeks I had APEL permanently on my mind — I had flashes of inspiration at odd times during the day/night (while vacuuming, taking the dog for a walk, cooking dinner etc) and I had to have a pad/pen nearby the whole time to jot these "treasures" down lest I forget them. While at work I found myself analysing what/why I do things — realising more and more that I could use even simple, taken for granted, tasks to provide evidence of my experience and ongoing learning. I used critical incident analysis a great deal in my APEL portfolio — thoughts of previous experiences crammed into my head and I had to analyse in depth why/what I had learnt from these (sometimes even minor incidents) but all of which had gradually built up my knowledge. The level of academic writing was new to me and I was pleased to attend "return to study" sessions.'

(The same claimant talking about peer support.)

'Throughout the APEL process I needed much support. I bounced ideas off a midwifery colleague on the same course (APEL module) as me. I also found it extremely useful to discuss ideas with other course members, work colleagues and teachers so that I could make sense of what I was trying to do.'

(Talking about the emotional labour of APEL.)

'We were warned about the peaks and troughs and, for me, this was very true. On some days I felt very low, confused and tired with it all, but also had periods of elation when I felt things were falling into place. However, I'm pleased (and very proud) to say that I was successful in my application for credits. APEL has worked for me and I'm delighted that now it is possible for previous experience and learning to be acknowledged and used in an academic way. I'm encouraging my colleagues to explore this route and will be pleased to offer them my support.'

Section 2: Illustrative examples

Example 1

As part of the ENB research project (Skinner *et al*, 1997) my colleague and I generated two examples of potential APEL claims. Though both were based upon real claimants, we modified them, to varying degrees, not just for anonymity purposes but in order to create interesting areas that might arouse comment. As part of the ENB project, these two fictitious accounts were presented to APEL advisers/assessors in a number of institutions and their comments collated. Recipients were asked to imagine that these represented no more than a preliminary presentation of a potential APEL claim which could, following their initial advice, be developed into a firm claim. It was clear that there were similarities between their comments in respect of each account. Account A was viewed as worthy of a greater volume of credit and at a higher academic level than account B. Account A was seen as more analytical, evaluative and reflective. While account B was descriptive, theoretical and academic in approach, the evidence was insufficiently focused.

One of these accounts (shown below and referred to as account A in the ENB report) had been used by me as part of a staff development programme for the eighteen months preceding the ENB project. It contains intentional spelling and grammatical errors. References, are fictitious and used purely to illustrate the candidates use of theory.

Those advisers/assessors who took part in the ENB research

commented as follows on the possible level of learning. It was generally felt to equate to level 2 or possibly level 3. The account was described as:

- systematic
- reflective
- analytical
- evaluative
- self-critical
- good application of knowledge to practice
- good variety of sources and breadth of information gathering
- didn't just accept theory at face-value but applied theory in a critical way
- proactive and innovative practice
- showed real learning.

Account A

After each paragraph of the account I have provided my own comments.

Paragraph 1: 'In 1991 I designed a health education package because I had found that a number of my patients appeared to be ignorant of basic food information and the implications of dietary habits on their health and well-being. They would often appear surprised when they discovered how many calories they consumed in a day compared with their needs and often had no idea of the salt content of different foods or what effect caffeine might have.'

Comment:

This sets the scene. It is not just descriptive: it offers insight into why this package was developed. It shows that the nurse discovered a potential problem, tried to find out more about it, and then took action to influence the situation. The health education pack will be essential evidence.

Paragraph 2: 'Although I had been introduced to health education and dietary needs in my initial preparation programme in 1985, I began the project by carrying out a literature search and visiting the health education section so that I could find out what work had been done before. I completed an annotated bibliography. One of the articles I read suggested that there was a link between social class and diet, as well as age and physical problems (*Eating for Life*). This seemed to support my findings and formed the basis for much of my work.'

Comment:

This shows that the claimant is able to retrieve data and is aware of the value of existing knowledge. The annotated bibliography will prove a useful piece of evidence. Since the pack was developed in 1991, a 1980 reference may be a little dated, particularly in an area in which change is rapid. Therefore, I would want to know why s/he had selected out this particular example of reading and would want to see, from the bibliography, that more recent works had informed her activities.

> Paragraph 2 contin: 'Statements such as those on page three of the pack I designed, and the questionnaire and quiz which accompany it, show that I have considered a diverse range of factors which influence diet.'

Comment:

We now have a questionnaire and quiz sheet to add to sources of **evidence**. I would like to see the claimant use a highlighter pen to direct the assessor's attention to words, lines which show consideration of a 'diverse range of factors', as claimed, in the pack (page 3), questionnaire and quiz.

> Paragraph 2 cont: 'Although quite a lot had been written, I found that it was mainly in poster form or didn't seem to offer the depth and breadth of information I thought would help. Sometimes the language was rather "medical" and at other times patronising. I surveyed a number of my friends and relations to see how they responded to different language and different ways of putting the same message across. I found that some of my younger friends read anything that was quick like a fast food packet and anything that took longer to read was unlikely to be considered. However, when in hospital one is somewhat confined for a time and may be grateful for reading materials. However, there was no point in effecting a change or intended change while my patients were in hospital if they did not follow it up outside. Therefore, I spent quite a lot of time looking at different advertisements and noting which made an impact on me and why. I found a book called *Getting Your Message Across* (Hohnson H, 1986). This book made a significant contribution to the way I chose to present the work.'

Comment:

I would like to see an example of something considered inadequate in depth or breadth or where terminology was felt to be inappropriate. The claimant could annotate this example, thus giving me further insight into his/her reasoning. This would form yet another piece of evidence of learning. Carrying out a survey shows that the claimant is aware of the value of the views of others but I would like to know how representative this sample was, eg. how close is the match between those in the sample and his/her patient group (just a brief statement is all that is needed) and what were the numbers involved. It does not matter that it was a very small sample — what matters is that the claimant is aware of the limitations of knowledge gained in this way. The claimant says patients may be grateful for reading materials when in hospital but, from his/her advantaged position (s/he has the opportunity to observe hospitalised patients) is this true? Do patients, for example, read any ward introductory materials, menus? It doesn't matter so much whether or not this observation was carried out; what matters is that the claimant recognises that, without this, the statement may not be factually correct or that, from casual, non-systematic observation, it appeared that patients were grateful for reading materials. An example of both informative and less useful advertising would be helpful supporting evidence. It may be that the claimant hasn't retained this sort of evidence. However, s/he can say that no examples have been kept but state that, because of this, s/he has provided examples taken from current materials available to her in order to illustrate the point.

> Paragraph 3: 'I also extended my knowledge on nutrition by reading journal articles and textbooks. I spent some time with the dietician. It was quite difficult to decide how much information was essential as well as which information fell into this category because if the package was too long it would be less likely to be read. Section 2 of the pack demonstrates this ability to select information which is essential but my knowledge is applied throughout. For example, if you looked at page 2 you would see that I have condensed some complex information about protein into five lines and a drawing. This took numerous drafts before I was happy with it and involved a number of hours work.'

Comment:

Which articles and textbooks? A bibliography is another useful source of evidence. The dietician's comments on this particular health education pack would be useful evidence, particularly if reference can be made to specific features of the pack such as choice of language/ terminology, information provided. Don't leave the assessor to rummage around looking for the example about protein which is, apparently, in section 2, page 2. Say that this has been highlighted in pink/yellow or whatever colour highlighter pen.

> Paragraph 4: 'I made out a list of all the ways in which the physical problems from which my patients suffered could influence their dietary needs. I did the same in relation to social and psychological factors. I did this so that I could get an overview of the kind of things I should consider when writing the pack. Although I didn't keep the list I believe the information and the way it is contained within the pack

demonstrate my awareness of the ways different factors influence diet. Once I had drafted an outline of the pack I talked to patients about it because I wanted to get their reactions. I had feedback which gave me reason to modify certain parts of it. For instance, a number of my patients didn't think I really knew what it was like to manage on very little money and seemed to think that you could not eat healthily if you were poor. As a result of this I found out about the benefit/pension levels and then went around the supermarkets working out exactly what I could get for a reasonable proportion of this. I also asked a number of patients what they spent on food each week. I obtained a number of booklets from the Advice Centre and picked out relevant information.'

Comment:

The list isn't available, so a few examples would help. Once again, don't leave the assessor to wander around in the pack trying to infer the claimants awareness of ways that different factors influence diet. Use the highlighter pen again to direct his/her attention or cite illustrative examples and direct his/her attention to these. (I once accompanied a community mental health nurse on a home visit. I listened carefully to the exchanges between client and nurse and was impressed with the apparent use of cognitive therapy techniques. At times, I inferred that the nurse was well-versed in risk assessment and had, at times, taken steps to provoke reactions as part of that assessment. However, away from the patient's home I discovered that what went on had been more by luck than judgement and that, in fact, some of what I perceived as well-planned risk taking was more like lack of thought. I know all about experts and habituation but I'm afraid that this was not the reason in this case. It was a lesson to me that I shouldn't see what I wanted to see, infer what I hoped was there, or take anything for granted.)

The claimant has made impressive use of real patients as informants and taken further action in the light of feedback. I'm longing to know whether it was true that s/he had underestimated the difficulties of managing on a tight budget and, if so, what this told him/her about his/her relationship to the socio-economic backgrounds/circumstances of his/her patients. This self-knowledge could give rise to further insights with respect to other assumptions being made by the nurse.

Paragraph 5: 'I decided to use an educative approach since the authoritarian/medical approach had not seemed to work, perhaps because people don't like doing what they are told, especially if they don't understand why it is important. This approach became known to me through a short course I attended in 1990 in X. This course helped me to realise that much of what I was saying and doing at the time was wasted since I had failed to listen to the verbal and non-verbal messages my patients were giving me. I learned to recognise my own values and beliefs and what lay behind them.'

Comment:

I would be concerned that the nurse states 'people don't like doing what they are told'. Could it be that some people in some situations do like doing what they are told? How does the sick role fit in with this statement? This statement is sweeping and needs modifying, explaining, referencing and so on, if the assessor is to be reassured that the nurse has based his/her work on sound knowledge. The course certificate, or any other form of confirmation of attendance, will be useful **evidence**. Good example of reflection and self-knowledge resulting from same but I'd like a relevant example of values and beliefs. If, for example, the nurse was in conversation with a colleague when she returned from the course the conversation might have gone something like this.

Nurse: *This course helped me. I learned to recognise my own values and beliefs and what lay behind them.*

Colleague: *What do you mean?*

Nurse: *Well, for example, I sort of thought that quite a lot of women were kind of irresponsible in the way they brought up their kids, particularly when it came to feeding them. You know — chips, chips and more chips. But then I started to think, well, I had a mum and dad and my gran lived with us. We used to make a big thing of meals and my dad would be really cross if my brother and I weren't there when the meal was ready. He'd say, 'If your mother can take the trouble to prepare it, then you can show her the courtesy of being ready for it'. But, mum had both my dad and my nan to back her up and she didn't go out to work. And, I admit, my kids get chips more than they should. I think this has influenced the way I've seen some of my patients and probably the way I've given the advice.*

Nobody is suggesting that claimants bare their souls to an unknown assessor but, if a claimant states recognition of own values and beliefs as pertinent to the way s/he produced a health education pack, then a brief example is helpful.

Paragraph 6: 'My package also shows that I was not only aware of the communication needs of my clients but also had an awareness of the range of different backgrounds from which they came. This is why I used large print and why I used examples of telly soaps and adverts which would be familiar or at least accessible to the majority. I was aware that I had to be very careful about including this type of example but I checked with the hospital administrator who looked at the package before it was finalised to ensure that it was not likely to get us into legal difficulties. Since I had a number of Asian patients I arranged for a local club to have the materials translated for me. This was extremely interesting and I learned that there were no words in Hindi for some of the words I used. I realised that I had frequently used these words with my Asian patients and they had politely smiled and acknowledged me but possibly not got the message since some of them had very little English. This exercise lead me to read more about patients from different cultural backgrounds and particularly their eating habits. My experience to date had been a curry or sweet-and-sour from the take-away. I had very little real idea what was eaten in a typical Indian home, if there was such a thing. What was the point of a leaflet on healthy eating if some of my patients were excluded from using it? At about this time I completed the ENB 998 (1992) and this added to my understanding of setting outcomes and using appropriate language.'

Comment:

While I can **guess** why the claimant used large print, I need to be told. The claimant gives a good rationale for taking the materials for checking by administration and for including a translated version. I would like to be directed to sections in the pack which were informed by the claimant's insights into Asian diets or, failing this, some further explanation. How did the claimant gain a better understanding of Asian diets? The ENB 998 certificate is, we assume, accredited under APL and, therefore, no credit will be recognised within this APEL claim (double-counting). However, it is perfectly legitimate to cite the contribution of this, or any other, course.

Paragraph 7: 'The package is now on its third revision. I give the package to patients as soon as they are admitted. This is because they may have odd moments when they could read it and if I don't give it to them until they go home it is likely to be filed away somewhere and forgotten. Also, while they are in hospital, I can mention the package and see how they scored on the questionnaire and the quiz. I included the quiz because health education should be fun because eating for many people is fun and therefore a dry, boring reinforcement of what they have possibly already been told will have little positive impact.'

Comment:

I would like to have insight into when and why the revisions were made, what changes were made and why? Good explanation of why it is given, when it is given, and the need for fun. The claimant has made use of learning theory (possibly from the ENB 998) and uses the quiz to reinforce learning and possibly motivate the patient to read.

Paragraph 7 contin: 'I believe that the pack is attractive in appearance, ie. the glossy cover and the colours. I have also encouraged some patients to make a list of food that they particularly like and dislike and then gone through this with them showing what their diet is rich in and deficient in. We look at substituting one food for another. This is particularly useful with diabetic clients and some of the older clients who have a reluctance to cook either because they are alone or they try to economise on fuel. I have also spoken with the dietician who has visited the ward when we have a patient who has a particular problem or who has expressed an interest in seeing her. She has a copy of my pack because it is important that we do not contradict each other. She is happy with it. After attending a half day session on food handling I added a bit more information on this to my pack.'

Comment:

Why does it matter whether it is attractive or not? If it does matter, this must be explained. A useful piece of evidence would be the likes and dislikes lists of one or two patients, with annotation concerning richness or deficiency and substitutes. One or two mini care studies in respect of diabetic clients or others would be useful evidence. Confirmation of half-day session as evidence. I would want to know what was added following the study session and why?

Paragraph 8: 'I believe that I achieved quite a lot with this package. I know a lot more about how to give information and how important it is, with health education, to be sure that the target group understand the message. I know now what my own failings were and how I based what I did on my own education and background. I certainly felt that I had made some impact on some of my patients. If I were to make recommendations to others on the basis of what I have learned from this experience I would say that they should try to do as much background reading as possible prior to even considering putting pen to paper. I was continually finding new information that I wished I had considered earlier. However, there has to be a cut off point but I know I would have felt more certain if I had allocated a period of, say, one month to do a literature search on the whole range of issues that I might need to consider. When I started I had no word processing skills and I developed these during the period of designing this package. When I started I was typing and then re-typing which was time consuming and wasteful but with word processing I could edit. I think that some of my colleagues were not as keen on this project as they might have been. This could be jealousy but it could also be because I didn't involve them enough in the beginning. I knew about "change theory" but I don't think I really paid as much attention to the need to unfreeze and then carry people with me. Maybe I should have consulted and involved them more rather than try to do so much on my own. I learned that I do not take enough advantage of having a team and this is something I must address in the future. I would like to think that now that we have a computer terminal on the ward it might actually be possible to have the pack on disk. This would be an attraction to the younger patients and maybe we could introduce some of the non-computer literate to IT while they are recovering.'

Comment:

A good paragraph on learning resulting from this experience. Useful reflections on how it could have been improved and lessons learned. Reference for 'change theory' required.

Paragraphs 9 and 10: 'I now lecture to students on "Approaches to health education" and refer to the pack in this session. The lecture is generally well received because they can see that it is something they can do themselves and I am certainly not an "academic". I intend to review the pack in another year and seek the views of users and staff with a view to modifying where necessary because food fads and eating patterns change, sometimes quite subtly over time, prices change and so on and my work would be stale.'

Comment:

Lecture notes are useful sources of evidence.

General comments

In my view, this has all the makings of a successful APEL claim. It will be improved by:

1.   Greater use of the explanatory words such as:

because... , if ... , unless... , however... , for example ... , this is illustrated by... , I realised that... , the assumption was... , the alternatives were... , the consequences might have been... (see *chapter 5*).

2.   Attention to spelling, grammar and paragraph boundaries.

3.   Organisation, structure and cross-referencing.

To help claimants organise their claim, I would suggest five things.

A. Claimants should imagine that they are invited to help a group of other nurses/midwives to learn what it is that they themselves have learned. The claimant begins by identifying what it is s/he has learned. In the case of our fictitious claimant s/he:

i)   has learned to appreciate the physical, psychological, social factors that make people eat the way they do

ii)   knows what makes a healthy diet

iii) knows a number of ways of influencing people with regard to what they eat

iv) can put together a dietary health education programme that is likely to be effective with more than just a small group of patients

v) can create teaching sessions to help other staff help patients with good diet programmes and greater understanding of the benefits.

We would reword these outcomes as follows:

1. Analyse the impact of biopsychosocial factors on nutrition.
2. Analyse the constituents of a well-balanced diet.
3. Devise strategies likely to influence the eating habits of patients.
4. Design and utilise a health education package appropriate to the needs of a wide range of patients.
5. Create a teaching programme to facilitate other members of staff in supporting/designing patient education programmes.

B. I would ask the claimant what the students would have to know and do in order to achieve each one of the outcomes. Since the claimant has already achieved these outcomes (and written them within her preliminary account presented above) s/he will know what s/he did, whether it was effective and how it could have been improved. This is rather like the demonstrator (see *chapter 5*) who gave us the benefit of her knowledge and insights to produce a culinary delight. The claimant is asked to become the teacher/demonstrator and to give the student the benefit of his/her knowledge and insight so that the student can build upon it. Some of the claimant's knowledge came from pre-existing sources and s/he can refer the student to these (why stand in front of a class and read something that students can read for themselves) but other knowledge has been generated by the claimant him/herself. These two forms of knowledge comprise a new baseline from which students can start. In this way professional knowledge is passed on from nurse/midwife to nurse/midwife and future generations.

C. I would ask the claimant to make a list of the teaching aids s/he will use (suggested **evidence**) and what it is that s/he will ask students to show as proof of any particular activity needed to develop the end product, ie. a health education pack on diet.

D. The claimant will need to identify what credit is being sought. For example, is s/he seeking general or specific credit (if so, matched against which module), how many credits and at which level.

E. Finally, I would need evidence that the claimant had, in fact, developed this package and utilised it in the way that s/he claims. A range of artefacts have been suggested as evidence. In the past, I have been handed assignments for 'traditional' assessment purposes (to date I have not, to the best of my knowledge, received a fraudulent APEL claim) that were not the work of the students who had submitted them. An unscrupulous claimant might present a piece of work, such as an information pack for patients, that had been developed by another person. Therefore, it is normal practice to require some form of testimony from a manager or colleague in addition to the range of evidence suggested above.

Example 2

The fictitious claimant cited in example 1 had the added advantage of being in possession of what might be called a 'solid artefact', ie. a health education package. This provided a tangible source of evidence. There are many more areas of nursing/midwifery around which claimants have no such luxury. These claims often involve the 'soft skills' of communication, interpersonal relationships or teamwork. The following brief extract from an APEL claim (anonymised) is one such case and involves the use of art as therapy, coupled with a counselling technique. The claimant provides an example of the way in which, in nursing/midwifery, we combine, blend and modify knowledge to inform our practice. One of the exercises I encouraged claimants to undertake was to highlight those specific words and phrases that they believed gave me, or their assessor, better insight into their thought processes and the underlying knowledge and reasoning informing actions. This activity frequently resulted in the claimant introducing a greater number of words such as **because, unless, if**, and phrases such as, **'as a result...'** and **'without this...'** I have italicised specific words and phrases that add to the richness of this extract:

> 'As part of my training, I had gained experience of the use of art as a means of expressing feelings and reflecting on them. Each member of the student group facilitated an 'art therapy' session in which we all participated and then reflected on its application in practice and how we'd felt ourselves. *I found this* a creative way to express my thoughts and I can still see in my own mind my drawings and how I'd felt at that time. One particular method was beneficial in reflecting on past experiences and then looking towards the future, identifying positive goals. This was the 'Road of Life'. I discussed this with x (patient) and she was keen to participate. *One of the most important aspects* of art therapy is that the patient must participate in her own treatment and thereby her own recovery. *I feel this was* an important aspect of x's agreement *because* it showed

commitment to change and *unless* this is present then it is less likely to be successful. I also discussed my idea with other members of the ward team and they were interested in this approach and felt it would be beneficial to x.

The 'Road of Life' involves literally drawing a road of your past life. It is flexible and creative in that the participant can use any visual pictures to signify how they felt at any particular stage in their life. This is less threatening as they only draw what they want to express. *An example* would be to use sharp bends in the road, hazard signs, trees, flowers, also weather, eg. clouds, sun, storms. I prepared for this session by setting time aside for myself and x in which we wouldn't be disturbed. *Issues to take into account* were on days when there was adequate staffing levels, in which I wasn't in charge and to stress the importance of us not being interrupted. Also a time when x was ready to look at her feelings. I acquired the equipment necessary, eg. large pieces of paper and coloured pens as colours can also signify feelings. We didn't set a time limit but *I was aware* not to allow the session to be too in-depth for a great amount of time so x could leave the session feeling comfortable and not distressed. I feel it is important to allow expression when the client is able and not to force an issue. "The actual process of painting helps to break down the defensive/defiant mechanisms that operate, particularly in the early stages of treatment" (Murphy, 1984). Although x hadn't presented as being "defiant" or "defensive", I didn't want to create or encourage any of these feelings. *I feel* that I may have done this if I'd concentrated on diet and weight gain, because we wouldn't have addressed the underlying issues and enabled x to work through these and regain an "undestructive" control of herself. The room I chose was quiet, light and couldn't be overlooked from the outside of the building. To encourage expression, I had large pieces of paper and we lay these on the floor. *I felt* small paper may limit drawings and so limit expression. The drawings could be as big or as small as she wished and I explained that she didn't need to fill the paper. I participated myself. I did this *because I felt* x would have some guidance on how to complete the exercise. Also, so as not to feel she was being observed, enabling her to feel more comfortable, I explained that I would be talking about my road of life but this wasn't to expect her to respond in a helping way. I ensured my drawing had good and bad times but that they were not too giving of myself that the emphasis did not focus on me. *I felt* that giving some information about myself would help to build trust within our relationship. *On reflection*, by doing my own road of life I might have created feelings within myself that were upsetting and, although I would not have shown them, it may have affected our session together. This didn't happen. However, *I would consider this point* when using this again and may not participate as fully. X was very creative when drawing. After we had finished our past road I briefly explained mine to her. I then allowed her to describe hers and what her art signified. I used the art work as guidance in my questions and encouraged her to explore further her feelings surrounding certain events. I concentrated on positive aspects because this would help to build on them when we were finding ways to cope. When she felt she had explored all she wished I asked her to draw a future road of life about how she wanted things to be and what she hoped to achieve. We then discussed this and looked at ways she could reach her aims and what might hinder her; why and how to overcome these obstacles or to set a more realistic aim. We then talked about how she'd felt doing this exercise... (The claimant goes on to explain how she combined art with a model of counselling.) Egan (1982) suggested that a way to help people resolve their problem and achieve a goal is to help them identify facilitating factors (their strengths) and restraining factors (hindrances), then to develop their strengths and find ways to overcome obstacles. This method helped this patient but *I don't feel* it would be appropriate for everybody with problems similar to x. Apart from the need to address a person's individual needs, *I don't feel it is always wise* to delve into the past to find a cause for certain problems, *unless* they wish to, as this *may* create problems that the client had not previously thought of as being problems. It can be just as beneficial to look at the presenting problem, why it happens now and find ways to change and cope. I found students were enthusiastic to know more about this approach so I did a teaching session in which they all participated in doing their own road of life, to reflect on how they felt, so as to be aware of possible feelings of clients. Also, the important aspect of finishing a session on a positive note, not leaving the client feeling hopeless.'

Example 3

In this example, a claimant was evidencing achievement of the outcomes of a compulsory module covering skill mix and human resource planning. I have listed below both the references and artefacts cited in the supporting commentary accompanying this claim.

References

Auld M (1976) *How Many Nurses? A Method of Estimating the Requisite Nursing Establishment for a Hospital.* Royal College of Nursing, London

Ball J (1988) *Dependency Levels In Delivery Suite.* Proceedings of the Research and the Midwife Conference, London

Ball J (1992) *Birth-rate Using Clinical Indicators for Assessing Workload, Staffing and Care Outcomes: An Extended and*

Revised Version of the Original Birth-rate Manual. Nuffield Institute for Health Services Studies, Leeds

Ball J (1993) Workload Measurements in Midwifery. In: Alexander J, Levey V, Roach S, (eds) *Midwifery Practice: A Research Based Approach.* Macmillan, Basingstoke: 155

Ball J, Gladstone L, Collier M (1984) *Criteria for Care: The Manual of the North West Staffing Levels Project.* Newcastle Polytchnic Products Ltd, Newcastle-upon-Tyne

Department of Health (1989) *A Strategy for Nursing.* HMSO, London

Department of Health (1993) *Changing Childbirth: The Report of the Expert Maternity Group.* HMSO, London

Department of Health (1994) *The Patients' Charter: The Maternity Services.* HMSO, London

Artefacts presented as evidence:

Confirmation of attendance on a two week management course

Yearly CDS statistics (five years)

Comparative analysis of CDS workload for two years

Three-monthly CDS workload statistics for one year

Monthly CDS workload statistics for one year

Graph demonstrating elective LSCS over three months

Critical incident demonstrating actual workload

CDS shift report

Birth-rate score sheet

Dependency criteria plan

CDS workload pattern over three shifts for three months

Results of workforce survey

Duty rota.

Below is one short extract from the supporting commentary concerning the final artefact, ie. duty rota:

'As is normal practice, it was drawn up three weeks in advance, with the knowledge that it might be subjected to alteration if circumstances changed during that period. When planning the roster in question (see item 12) with an aim of maximum possible efficiency and effectiveness, I took into consideration the skills and availability of all the CDS staff; the financial costs of the various grades; the workload variation (of which I had extensive knowledge); annual leave; absences due to sickness and education.

... For all the remaining early shifts, late and night duties, five midwives were allocated per shift to ensure safe cover. The principles behind this skill mix saw one G grade sister taking charge of the shift, F grade being responsible for theatre cases and teaching students and midwives to acquire theatre skills and three E grade midwives to manage the workload in the delivery suite. An additional G grade would be on duty for theatre mornings to provide extra support for E grade midwives. As the night duty is a demanding ten hour span, two sisters were designated to share the overall responsibilities of the unit.

Nursing auxiliaries were deployed on all shifts to carry out non-midwifery tasks in order to enable midwives to spend more time providing quality care for clients. In cases of absence, due to staff sickness and/or normal staff shortages during any particular shift, the senior midwife would be notified to allow the possibility of deployment of midwives (if there were extra staff) from other wards to CDS. I am aware that clients on CDS need acute care but I appreciate that postnatal areas' staffing requirements also need consideration (to ensure safe care for mothers and babies) before any midwives could be provided for CDS. However, if no ward was able to supply a midwife, a "bank" midwife would then be employed.

The overlap period in the afternoon was employed constructively as a time for the ward meeting and in-service sessions for teaching students and junior midwives. Ward meetings are important for the dissemination of information from management, the discussion of ward issues and the social interaction of all staff, which is essential if a work-conducive and happy atmosphere is to be achieved.'

This was a great deal of knowledge from a midwife who thought she was being a bit 'cheeky' claiming a management module when she didn't have a **certificate** in that subject.

And finally...

I would like to leave you with a piece of encouragement. All the nurses and midwives who have been cited in this text have completed degrees. Their marks have been very good and their ability to apply themselves to the tasks set has been outstanding. One particular student stands out in my mind because she so typified the ambivalence shown by nurses/midwives. Sometimes she felt that she was due the credit but at others, she felt she lacked the ability to gain a degree. She experienced the almost inevitable peaks and troughs of an APEL claim but, as a result of a succcessful outcome, embarked upon her chosen course (an honours degree) with a slightly greater confidence. She was older than most of the students and told me that she felt more like their mother. Her results from taught modules within the degree ranged between 57%–87% with an average of 71%.

I hope that this book has helped you understand AP(E)L and that you feel motivated to **go for it** and get all the credit you deserve.

References

Boud D, Keogh R, Walker D (1985) *Reflection: Turning Experience into Learning*. Kogan Page, London

Benner P (1984) *From Novice to Expert: Excellence and Power in Clinical Nursing Practice*. Addison-Wesley, California USA

Borner J, Suttcliffe A (1980) *Eating for Life*. MacCauley Press, London

English National Board (1991) *Framework for Continuing Professional Education for Nurses, Midwives and Health Visitors: A Guide to Implementation*. ENB, London

English National Board (1992) *Adding up the Past. APL/APEL: Guidelines for Good Practice*. ENB, London

Kolb D, Fry R (1975) Towards an applied theory of experiential learning. In: Couper CL (ed) *Theories of Group Processes*. J Wiley, Chichester

Kolb D (1984) *Experiential Learning*. Prentice Hall, New Jersey, USA

Nganasurian W (1995) Life in the Shadow of Supernurse. *Nurs Stand* 9(25): 54–55

Nganasurian W (1996) *AP(E)L in the Context of Health Care Today: Meeting the Needs of Nurses and Midwives*. Conference Paper presented to AP(E)L in Higher Education Conference, University of Ulster (to be published in 1999)

Reed J, Proctor S (1993) *Nurse Education: A Reflective Approach*. Edward Arnold, London

Skinner J, Nganasurian W, Pike S *et al* (1997) *An Investigation into the Reliability and Validity of Assessment Strategies for the Accreditation of Prior Learning of Nurses, Midwives and Health Visitors*. English National Board for Nursing, Midwifery and Health Visiting, London

Taylor M (1997) *Selected Poems*. Anglia Polytechnic University, Chelmsford

United Kingdom Central Council (1990) *The Report of the Post Registration Education and Practice Project (PREPP)*. UKCC, London

United Kingdom Central Council (1994) *The Future of Professional Practice — The Council's Standards for Education and Practice Following Registration*. UKCC, London

Index

A

academic award 5
academic credit 55
academic level 59
academic level 162
academic level 262
academic level 363
academic writing skills 4
accreditation (or assessment) of
    prior experiential learning
    (APEL)   19, 20
    what is APEL? 17
accumulating credit 4
acronyms xi
admission with credit   18
admitted with credit 13
advanced standing 12
alternative entry gate 17
AP(E)L advisor's role   23
AP(E)L assessor's role   23
AP(E)L portfolio 33
assessment 10, 68

C

certificate 43
certificated learning 43–44
challenge method 20
challenging assumptions 56
choosing a course 38
claimant's role 21
claimants support network 24
classification 6
collating materials into an APEL
    portfolio 67
consequences of an AP(E)L
    claim 26
context relevant credit 25

credit transfer tariff 47
cross-referencing evidence 65
currency of learning 46
currency of the learning 60

D

double- counting 21, 60
double-counting 27
dual accreditation 6

E

evidence 20, 22, 67
evidence of prior experiential
    learning 20
experience of APEL 70
experience v experiential learning
    25
experiential learning 53
experiential learning claim 58
Experiential Learning Cycle 54

F

flexible Learning 8

G

gather evidence of learning 63
general credit 18, 39, 47
general v specific credit 18

H

higher degree 6

I

identification of prior learning 32
identifying learning 62
integral part of an academic award
    18
interdisciplinarity 8

L
learning outcomes 3
levels of credit 3

M
mapping 39, 47

N
number and level of academic
    credit 48

O
outcomes of specific modules 59

P
pathway 5
payment 11
plagiarism 10
portfolio 20
postgraduate studies 6
price of AP(E)L 24
principle xii
prior certificated learning 19, 42
professional awards 5
professional portfolio 20, 28
professional progress 57

R
recognition of prior learning 20
referencing system 10
reflection 53
relevance 47
relevant knowledge and skills 39
relevant learning 67

S
sell-by date 64
specific credit 18, 47
specific modules 39
specific outcomes 67
standard of written English 10
statement of attendance 45
style of learning 9
substitute for specific learning 18

T
tariff 2
terminology x, xii
top-up degree 59
transferring credit 6

U
undergraduates 5
underpinning knowledge 64
updating 60

W
written commentary 65